£7.25

Printed and published by D. C. Thomson & Co. Ltd.,
185 Fleet Street, London EC4A 2HS.
ISBN 1 84535 151 7

DESPERATE DAN
HOWDY, ZEKE!
HI, DAN!
BEST GIT HOME.
HOBBLE! LIMP!
DAN'S HURT! DAN'S HURT!
DAN'S HURT!
DAN'S HURT!
DAN'S HURT!
DAN'S HURT!
ZEB AND PRUDY WUZ SMOOCHIN' LAST NIGHT!
ZEB AND PRUDY WUZ SMOOCHIN' LAST NIGHT!
ZEB AND PRUDY... WHAT?
I MEAN, DAN'S HURT, PRUDY.
BETTER!

WHAT'RE YOU ALL WHISPERIN' ABOUT?
GRAB!
HOBBLE!
DAN'S HURT!
DAN'S HURT!
I JUST GOT ME A STONE IN MY BOOT. IT CAN'T REALLY HURT NOBODY!
AW, JUST A STONE? PITY!
SIGH! JUST A STONE? OH, WELL!
WELL THAT'S NICE, I DON'T THINK. PESKY STONE!
FLICK!
WATCH THIS STONE, READERS!
WHAP!

THE STONE HAS MADE THE HORSE LASH OUT!
BLACKSMITH
KICK!
OOF!
OUCH!
WATCH THIS HAMMER!
WHAT THE...?
SLAM!
TESCUW
HIM MOCKING OUR TRIBAL DANCES!
THROB!
HOP!
HOP!
HOP!
HOP!
HELP!
GET HIM!

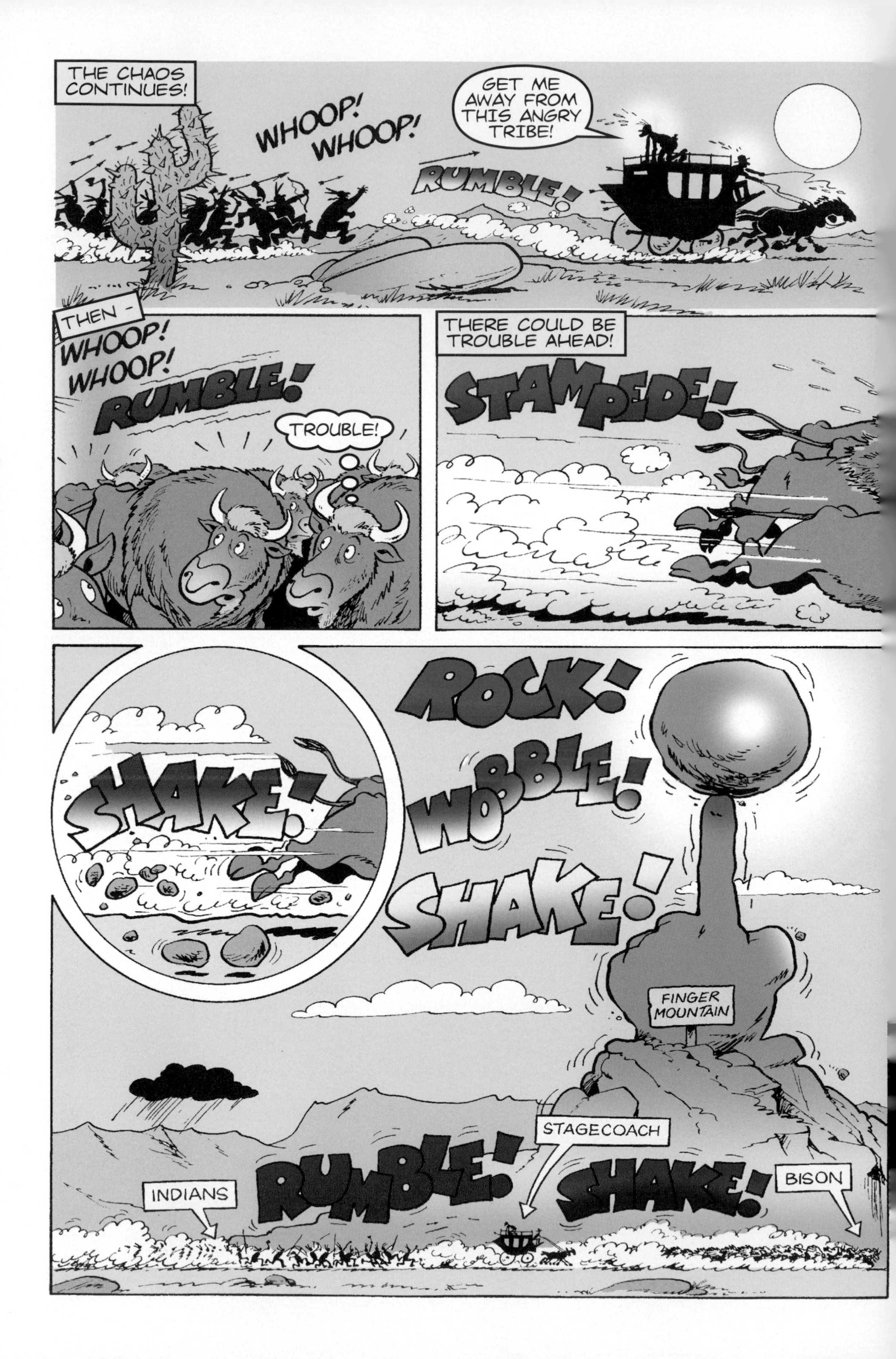
THE CHAOS CONTINUES!
WHOOP! WHOOP!
GET ME AWAY FROM THIS ANGRY TRIBE!
RUMBLE!
THEN -
WHOOP! WHOOP!
RUMBLE!
TROUBLE!
THERE COULD BE TROUBLE AHEAD!
STAMPEDE!
SHAKE!
ROCK!
WOBBLE!
SHAKE!
FINGER MOUNTAIN
STAGECOACH
RUMBLE!
SHAKE!
INDIANS
BISON

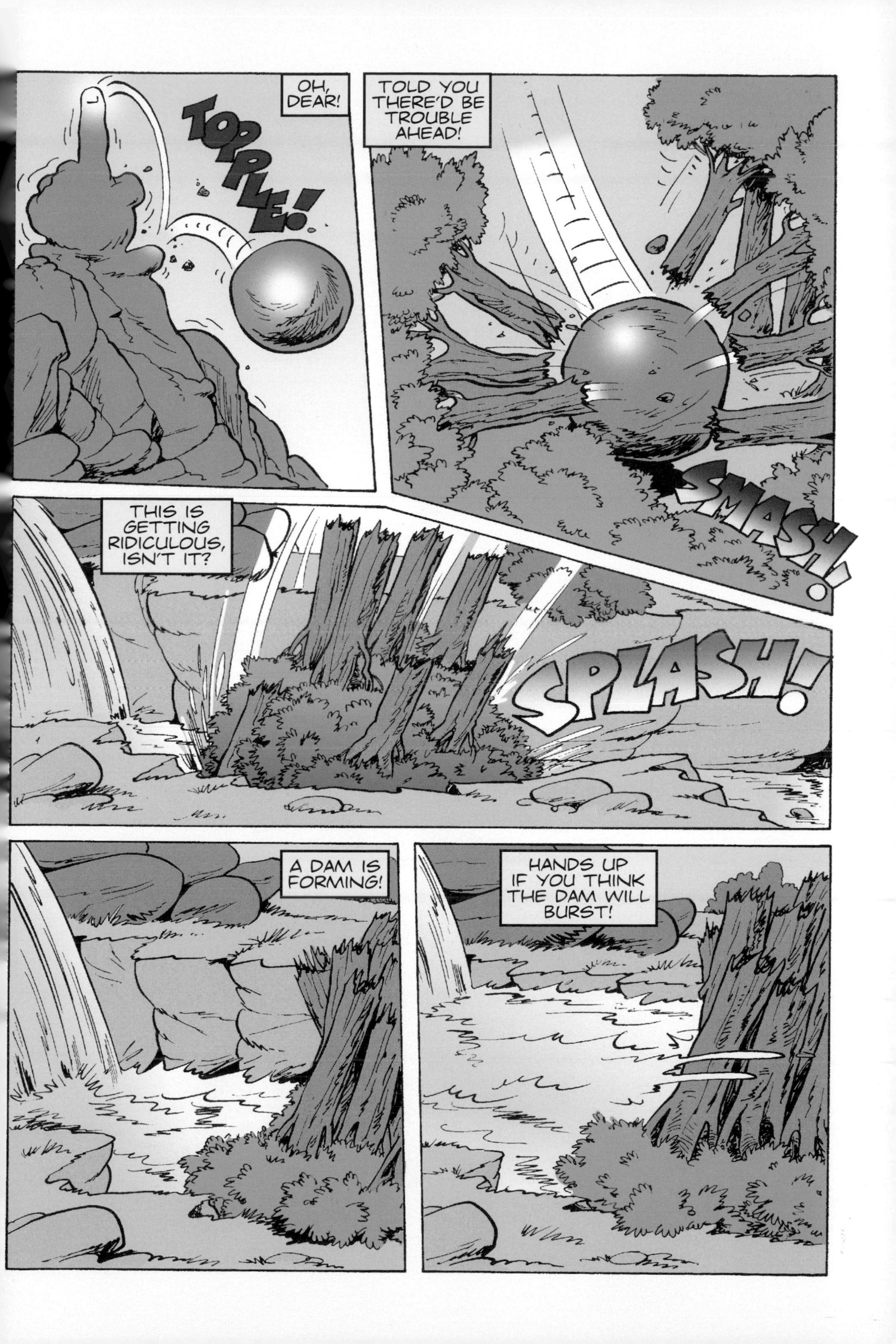
OH, DEAR!
TOPPLE!
TOLD YOU THERE'D BE TROUBLE AHEAD!
SMASH!
THIS IS GETTING RIDICULOUS, ISN'T IT?
SPLASH!
A DAM IS FORMING!
HANDS UP IF YOU THINK THE DAM WILL BURST!

YOU WERE RIGHT!
BURST!
WHAT A TERRIBLE CATASTROPHE!
HANKS
SALOON
WHOOSH!
THIS IS GREAT - I NEEDED A SHOWER!
BLAST!
ONE LITTLE STONE? CAN'T HURT NOBODY? HUH!
ER... OOPS!
KEN.H.HARRISON.

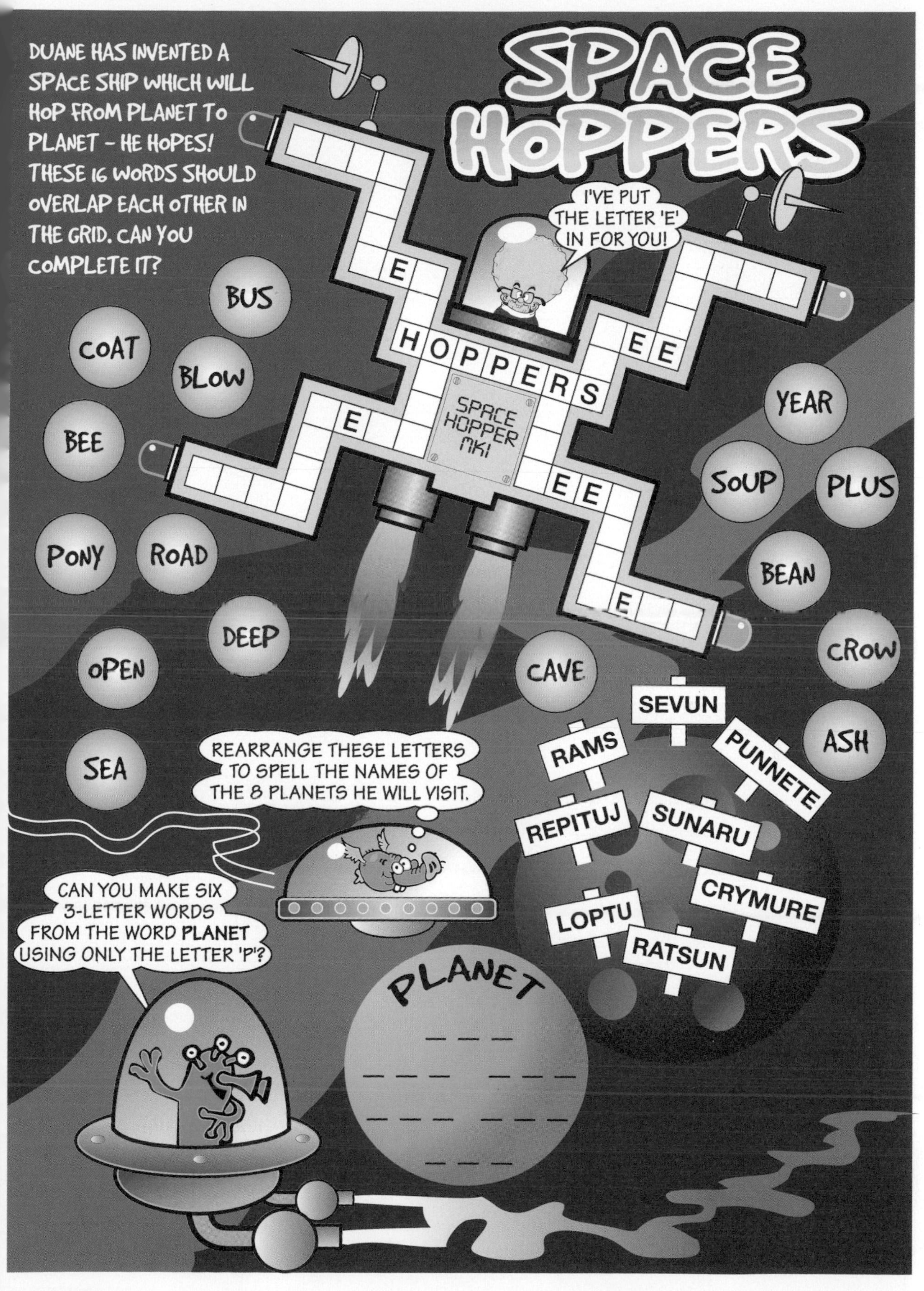

DAN/15-04
Gall & Strachan

Answers: Planets MARS, VENUS, NEPTUNE, JUPITER, URANUS, PLUTO, MERCURY, SATURN.
Words from Planet PAN, PEA, PET, PAL, PAT, PEN.

OWEN GOAL
WE'VE GOT AN IMPORTANT MATCH THIS AFTERNOON.
YOU'RE LISTENING TO DULL FM! NOW, THE WEATHER!
SMILE! IT'S FRIDAY (UNLESS IT'S NOT — IN WHICH CASE, DON'T SMILE)
THE BEANO — IT'S LIKE THE DANDY (BUT NOT AS GOOD!) — Signed, The Dandy Editor
NIGEL PARKINSON
HEAVY RAIN EXPECTED LATER!
OH, NO! THE GAME COULD BE RAINED OFF!
LADIES DON'T
Menswear
MENSWEAR
GENTS GEAR ON SALE
COATS! PANTS! VESTS! WE GOT 'EM!!
I'VE GOT AN IDEA!
NEXT, A MAN WITH A COLLECTION OF ANTIQUE DISHCLOTHS!
HI, GUYS! I'VE, ERM, GOT A NEW BIT OF KIT FOR YOU ALL.

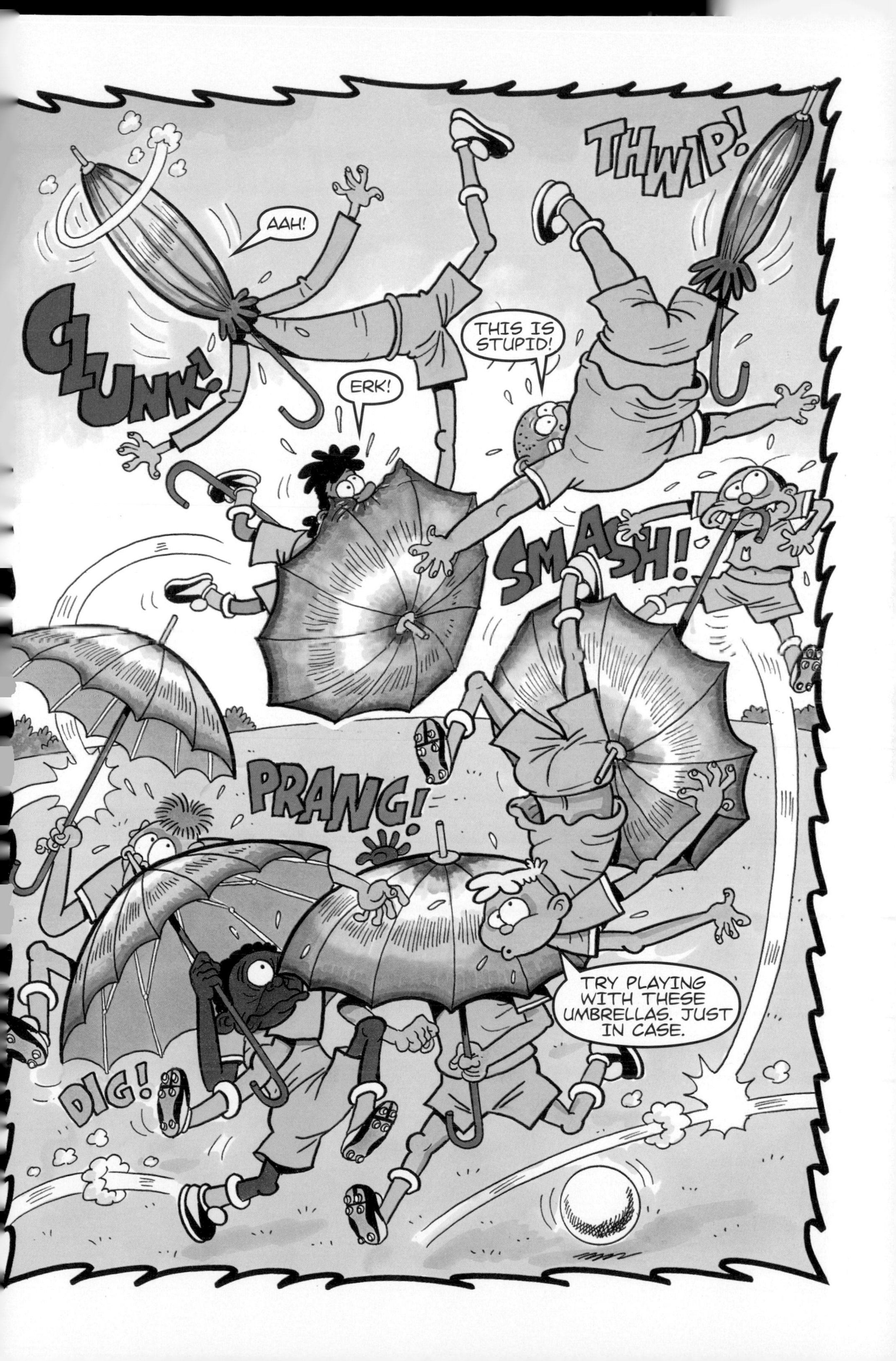
THWIP!
AAH!
CLUNK!
THIS IS STUPID!
ERK!
SMASH!
PRANG!
TRY PLAYING WITH THESE UMBRELLAS. JUST IN CASE.
DIG!

TRY THESE INSTEAD. IT LOOKS CLOUDY!
HAVE YOU GOT ONE IN MY SIZE?
ARGH!
CLANK!
TWANG!
TRIP!
HOOF!
TUMBLE!
OOF!
CRUMP

RUMBLE!
NOOO! A THUNDERSTORM!
NAH, JUST MY TUMMY RUMBLING. HAVEN'T HAD MY FIRST PIE OF THE DAY YET.
COACH OF THE YEAR - 1981
I MIGHT HAVE KNOWN.
ERM, WHY ARE YOU ALL WEARING RAINCOATS?
DURGH! WHY DO YOU THINK, COACHIE? IT'S GONNA RAIN!
OWEN, DID YOU CHECK YOUR FIXTURE LIST? WE'RE PLAYING AWAY FROM HOME TODAY!
ARE WE?
AND WE'RE PLAYING INDOORS!
GROAN! I FEEL UNDER THE WEATHER NOW!

WINKER WATSON
LED BY WINKER AND SALLY, THE BOYS AND GIRLS OF GREYTOWERS SCHOOL ARE IN THE MIDDLE OF A FULL-ON WATER FIGHT.
EAT WATER, SALLY.
AARRGH! THAT'S COLD.
CEASE FIRE IMMEDIATELY!!
MR CREEP, THE BOYS' FORM MASTER. MISS SNYDE, THE GIRLS' TEACHER.
STOP ALL THIS NONSENSE AND PAY ATTENTION! WE TEACHERS ARE GOING TO VISIT BOGMUIR SCHOOL IN THE FAR SCOTTISH HIGHLANDS.
YO!
RESULT, TROTTY! THE TWO ANTIQUES WILL BE GONE FOR WEEKS.
IT'S AN EDUCATIONAL TRIP SO WE'LL BE TAKING ALONG THREE LUCKY PUPILS.
NO, PLEASE NO...
WATSON, TROTTER, SALLY - GET PACKING!
BUT, SIR, WE... ER... HAVEN'T GOT ANY PASSPORTS!
STOP ARGUING, WATSON. THE DECISION IS FINAL!
AND DON'T FORGET YOUR SCHOOL BOOKS - THIS WILL BE A WORKING HOLIDAY!

NEXT DAY -
COME ALONG, YOU THREE! STOP DAWDLING AND GET OUR LUGGAGE ON THE TRAIN!
PUFF! ROTTERS!
AND -
WE'VE BROUGHT ALONG SOME TREATS FOR THE JOURNEY - MATHS, GEOGRAPHY AND HISTORY!
GROAN!
TWO HUNDRED MILES OF BOREDOM LATER -
TIME FOR A BREAK - YOU THREE MUST BE PECKISH BY NOW.
YAY! THE BUFFET CAR!
HARDLY, WATSON! MISS SNYDE AND I HAVE MADE YOU UP SOME NICE, NUTRITIOUS SANDWICHES.
PIG'S EAR PATÉ OR EGG AND RHUBARB?
THESE ARE WELL NASTY, MATE!
YEAH! AND THEY'RE HAVING A RIGHT OLD FEAST!
SO, IN THE NORTH OF SCOTLAND -
BE CAREFUL WITH MY VANITY CASE, WATSON!
VANITY CASE? I THOUGHT IT WAS A TOOL BOX!
FINALLY...
BOGMUIR HIGH SCHOOL
OH, I SAY! IT'S ABSOLUTELY LOVELY!
WHAT? IT'S SO HORRIBLE IT MAKES GREYTOWERS LOOK LIKE A FUN PARK!

CLARENCE, DIDN'T YOU SAY YOUR COUSIN WAS A TEACHER HERE?
THAT'S RIGHT...
...MACCREEP!
HULLOO!
SO, YOU'VE COME TO SEE HOW A PROPER SCHOOL OPERATES?
RUDE MAN!
LOOK AT YOUR WEEDY WEE PUPILS
GASP! NO ROOF IN THE DORM - IT'S FREEZING!
LET'S HAVE THE SCHOOL SONG FOR OUR GUESTS!
SURELY NOT!
MATHS, MATHS, GLORIOUS MATHS! WE LOVE MATHS AND TAKING COLD BATHS!
THAT'S WHAT I CALL WELL-BEHAVED!
LESSONS TO BE LEARNED HERE, METHINKS!
AT EASE, BOYS!
THEY'RE COMPLETELY OBEDIENT AND THEY'RE GIVING CREEP IDEAS!

WHEN THE TEACHERS ARE GONE...
YOU LOT ARE RIGHT UNDER THE THUMB. DON'T YOU EVER MISBEHAVE?
BEST ASK ARCHIE MACFRY, HE'S THE SCHOOL WANGLER!
LAST WINTER I MADE A SNOWMAN THAT LOOKED LIKE MACCREEP!
SORRY, MATE! THAT'S JUST SAD!
LAST WEEK I SWAPPED MACCREEP'S SOAP WITH A LUMP OF CHEESE!
LEAD N' BOULDERS
HO-HO! HE ENDED UP GRILLING IT FOR HIS SUPPER!
WOEFUL!
YOU NEED SOME HELP FROM AN EXPERT, ARCHIE!

NEXT MORNING -
RISE AND SHINE, BRATS! MISTER MACCREEP'S TAKING US ON A HIKE, SO BOOTS ON!
AND DON'T FORGET YOUR MIDGE REPELLENT - THE WEE BEASTIES ARE A BIT SAVAGE THIS TIME OF YEAR!
WATCH AND LEARN, ARCHIE! WE TAKE MACCREEP'S MIDGE REPELLENT AND SWAP IT FOR MISS SNYDE'S BUNION CREAM!
LATER -
PHEW! I'M EXHAUSTED - THIS MOUNTAIN'S WELL STEEP!
SOFT LADDIE - THIS IS JUST A WEE HILL!
MAYBE A SKIRL O' THE PIPES WILL KEEP YOUR SPIRITS UP!
CRIKEY! WHAT A DISMAL DIRGE!
IN THE NEXT GLEN -
MIDGES AHEAD! TIME TO PUT THE REPELLENT ON.
THAT'S THE STYLE. LASH IT ON!

WHAT'S THIS? THEY'RE HEADING STRAIGHT FOR US!
OO!
OW!
YEEK!
THAT'S WHAT YOU CALL A PROPER WANGLE, ARCHIE!
YOU'RE RIGHT, WINKER. THAT BUNION CREAM'S ATTRACTING THEM!
I SMELL A WANGLE! AS PUNISHMENT YOU CAN CARRY OUR KNAPSACKS!
SIGH!
LATER -
NOW FOR A WEE TREAT - A TOUR OF THE LOCAL PORRIDGE FACTORY!
MACGRUEL'S
GROAN!
SO -
BORING!
THIS IS WHERE WE MIX THE OATS AND WATER...
HEY, ARCHIE! LET'S LIVEN THINGS UP!
AYE! LET'S PRESS A FEW BUTTONS!
AND -
GLUB
SPLUDGE
TEE-HEE! SUCCESS!
HELP! MAD PORRIDGE ON THE LOOSE!

AS A PUNISHMENT YOU BOYS WILL EAT THE WHOLE PILE OF PORRIDGE.
EH?
AND WITH NO SUGAR. JUST SALT AND VINEGAR.
GROOO!
SOON -
HERE'S THE LAST STOP. THE HAGGIS FARM.
AYE, I'LL INTRODUCE YOU.
MAC DUFF'S HAGGISES!
WHAT KIND OF HAGGIS ARE THEY, MR MACDUFF?
WEST HIGHLAND WINDBREAKERS, MA'AM. THE VERY FINEST.
THIS ONE WOULD LOOK GOOD WITH CHIPS.
THEY LOOK WELL FIERCE. CHECK THE TEETH.
THEY'RE PERFECTLY SAFE.
AS LONG AS THEY NEVER HEAR THE BAGPIPES. THAT TURNS THEM A BIT MENTAL.
IS THAT SO... HMM!
ARE YOU THINKING WHAT I'M THINKING, ARCHIE?
GUESS SO, BUDDY.

I'LL FIT THIS HOSE TO THE BAG-PIPES...
...SO WE CAN STAND BACK AND WATCH THE FUN. PUFF!
AWFUL NOISE!
SQUEAK!
SQUAWK!
SQUEAL!
WAIL!
SKIRL!!
SQUEAL!
HOINK!
SQUARK!
GASP! THE HAGGIS HAVE GONE BERSERK.
EEEEK! BEASTLY CREATURES!
CALL MR MACDUFF!
I'M EVER SO SORRY.
NO APOLOGIES NEEDED! IT'S THE FAULT OF THESE BAD PUPILS.
WHO WILL NOW BE SENT TO THEIR DORM WITHOUT SUPPER.
YOU HEARD HIM - GET MOVING, RABBLE.
SO, LATER -
COOL WANGLES, WINKER - BUT LOOK WHERE IT'S GOT US.
DON'T GIVE UP, ARCHIE. IT'S EVERY SCHOOLBOY'S DUTY TO TRY AND TRY AND TRY TO OUTWIT TEACHERS.
MORE HIGHLAND HOOTS AND WANGLES COMING UP AHEAD.
SW©5

FORDHAM'S FOREIGN LEGION
NON-LEAGUE FORDHAM TOWN FOOTBALL CLUB HAD MANY FOREIGN PLAYERS BIG MONEY SIGNINGS? NO, A GROUP OF YOUNG IMMIGRANTS HAVE SETTLED IN FORDHAM AND DECIDED TO REVIVE THE RUN-DOWN CLUB.
STAFF ONLY
THIS SATURDAY THERE WAS GREAT EXCITEMENT. FORDHAM HAD DRAWN PREMIER LEGUE CHIDSEA IN THE CUP.
PIZZA
HEY, MIKO - A MAN HAS JUST DELIVERED BAGS OF CEMENT. WHAT'S THAT ABOUT?
WE'RE NEEDING IT TO SORT UP THE CANTEEN. WE'LL SELL DOZENS OF PIZZA TODAY TO PAY FOR IT, SILVAN.
ALL THE YOUNG PLAYERS HELPED AT THE CLUB.
GET SOME MORE FLOUR, SILV - I'M GONNA MAKE HUNDREDS OF PIZZA.
HEY, BRANYO - HELP BRING US IN MORE FLOUR.
WILL DO!
FLOUR
CEMENT
CEMENT
CEMENT

BRANYO WAS A GOOD PLAYER BUT HIS ENGLISH WAS VERY POOR.
THIS NO PROBLEM TO BRANYO.
CEMENT
CEMEN
GET THE FLOUR IN TO THE MIXERS - I'LL DO ANOTHER BATCH BEFORE WE HAVE TO GET KITTED.
FLOUR
CEMENT
FLOUR
FLOUR
THAT'S IT DONE! NOW LET'S CONCENTRATE ON THE CUP.
I CAN'T WAIT.
FRED KENT WAS FORDHAM'S UNPAID MANAGER.
STAY CONFIDENT, BOYS. YOU'RE YOUNG - BUT YOU'RE ALL GOOD PLAYERS.
NOW LET'S GO GET THEM, GUYS.

MIDFIELDER REVELLO WAS A CHIDSEA STAR.
HE'S A REALLY GOOD PLAYER...
...BUT NOT AS FAST AS ME.
HEY, KID...
...YOU'RE GOING THE WRONG WAY.

NO, I'M NOT!
HEY - HE'S GOT CLASS AS WELL AS SPEED.
AT HALF-TIME THERE WAS STILL NO SCORE.
REVELLO, LURE THAT SPEEDY KID INTO A RASH TACKLE. THEN PING A GOAL FROM THE FREE KICK.
SECOND HALF.
REVELLO IS GONNA TRY TO DO ME ON THE OUTSIDE.
JUST MADE IT!
HE-EY!
FREE KICK! DANGEROUS PLAY, MIKO CZECH.
BUT I GOT THE BALL.
YOU'RE TOO QUICK FOR YOUR OWN GOOD, SON.
ME QUICK? YOU'RE ABOUT TO SEE SPEEDO, OUR KEEPER.
8

REVELLO TOOK THE FREE KICK AND HIT A ROCKET.
NOBODY SAVES THAT.
THE KID'S GOT IT! AMAZIN'!
AS MIKO KNEW FROM TRAINING, SPEEDO HAGI WAS SUPER-QUICK.
FONY
LDE ELAINE

NOT ALL THE FAST ACTION WAS ON THE PITCH. AT THE SERVERY, MIKO'S PIZZAS WERE FLYING FROM THE OVEN.
THREE MORE MARGARHITAS.
PIZZA
PIZZA
PIZZA
HEY! THIS PIZZA'S BRICK HARD!
SO IS MINE!
GIVE'S OUR MONEY BACK. YOUR PIZZA'S ARE SOLID.
ER - THE SERVERY IS NOW C-CLOSING.
FLAMIN' CHEATS. OPEN UP!
PIZZ
BACK ON THE FIELD, MIKO AND THE BOYS HAD DECIDED TO ATTACK.
IF I CAN GET THIS BY HIM I'M IN ON GOAL.

AGH! FOUL!
MIKO AND THE BOYS HAD WORKED HARD AT FREE KICKS ON THE TRAINING GROUND.

GOAL!
YES!
CHIDSEA WERE STUNNED AND WITH ONLY FOUR MINUTES REMAINING FORDHAM HELD OUT TO RECORD A SHOCK WIN!
HEY, PIZZA BOYS. WHY ARE YOU NOT CELEBRATING?
'ERM, MIKO. SLIGHT PROBLEM.

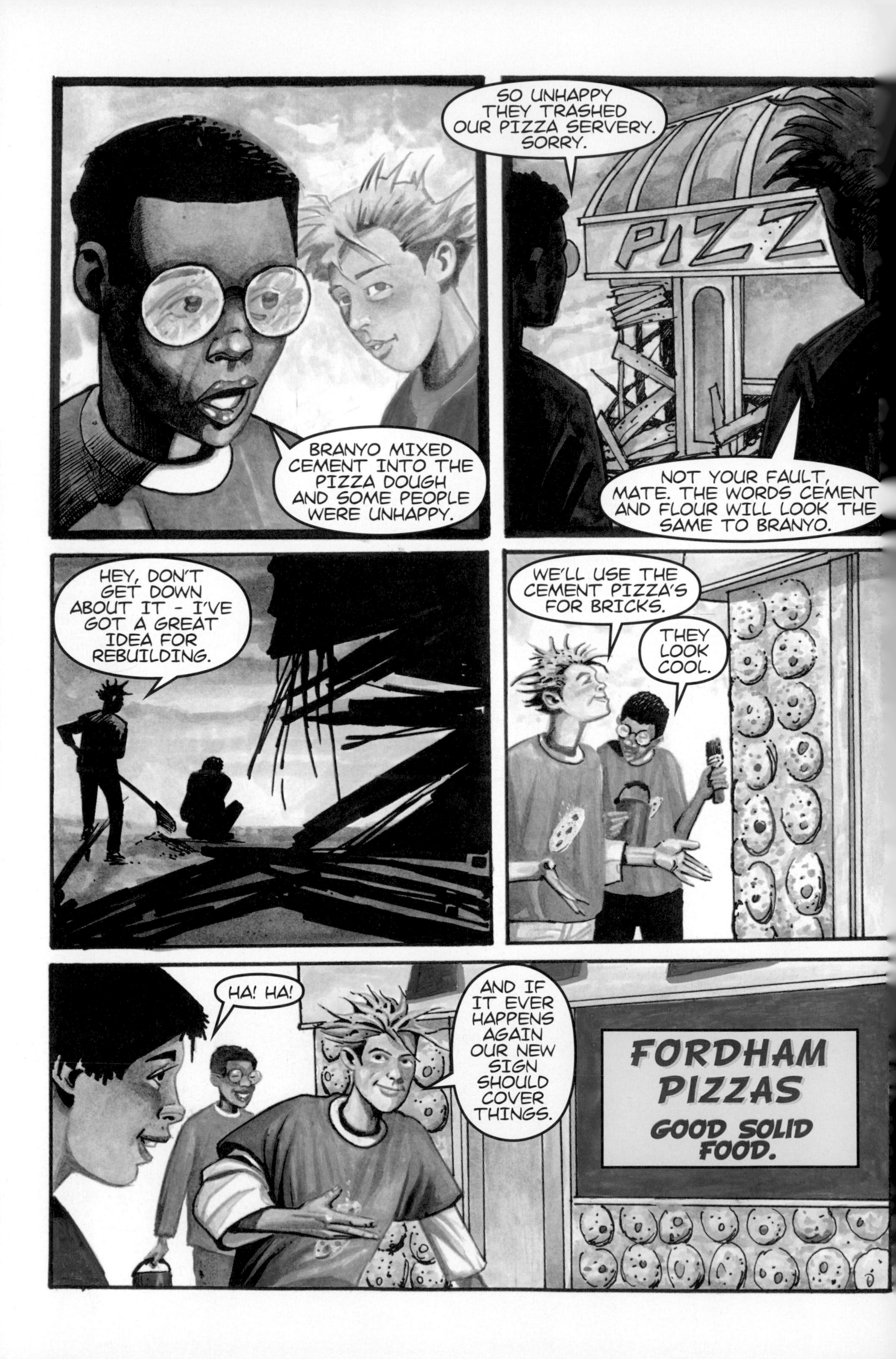
BRANYO MIXED CEMENT INTO THE PIZZA DOUGH AND SOME PEOPLE WERE UNHAPPY.
SO UNHAPPY THEY TRASHED OUR PIZZA SERVERY. SORRY.
PIZZ
NOT YOUR FAULT, MATE. THE WORDS CEMENT AND FLOUR WILL LOOK THE SAME TO BRANYO.
HEY, DON'T GET DOWN ABOUT IT - I'VE GOT A GREAT IDEA FOR REBUILDING.
WE'LL USE THE CEMENT PIZZA'S FOR BRICKS.
THEY LOOK COOL.
HA! HA!
AND IF IT EVER HAPPENS AGAIN OUR NEW SIGN SHOULD COVER THINGS.
FORDHAM PIZZAS
GOOD SOLID FOOD.

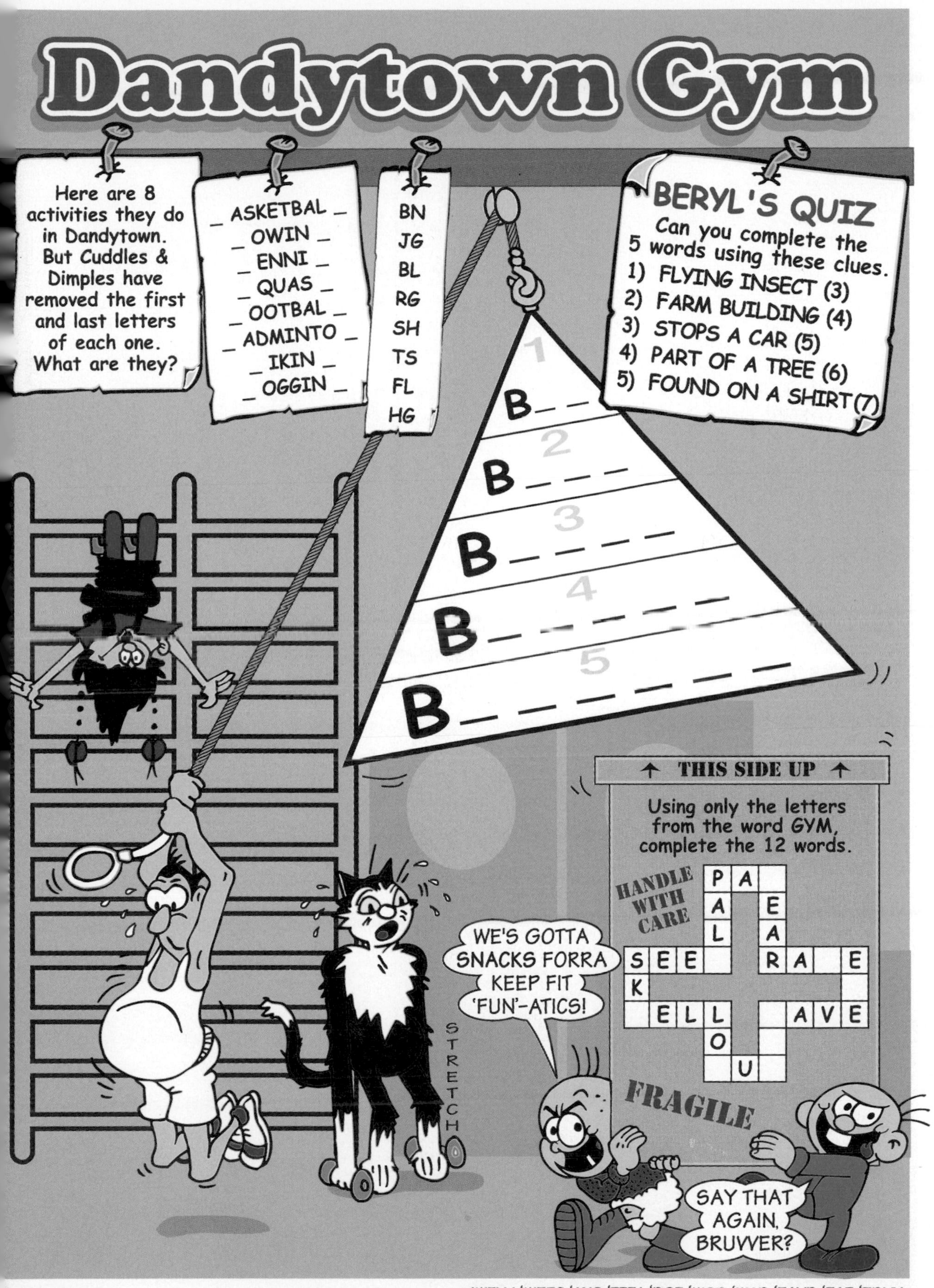

Dandytown Gym
Here are 8 activities they do in Dandytown. But Cuddles & Dimples have removed the first and last letters of each one. What are they?
_ ASKETBAL _
_ OWIN _
_ ENNI _
_ QUAS _
_ OOTBAL _
_ ADMINTO _
_ IKIN _
_ OGGIN _
BN
JG
BL
RG
SH
TS
FL
HG
BERYL'S QUIZ
Can you complete the 5 words using these clues.
1) FLYING INSECT (3)
2) FARM BUILDING (4)
3) STOPS A CAR (5)
4) PART OF A TREE (6)
5) FOUND ON A SHIRT (7)
1 B_ _
2 B_ _ _
3 B_ _ _ _
4 B_ _ _ _ _
5 B_ _ _ _ _ _
THIS SIDE UP
Using only the letters from the word GYM, complete the 12 words.
HANDLE WITH CARE
FRAGILE
PA
PAL
EAR
SEE
RA E
SK
ELL
AVE
LO
U
STRETCH
WE'S GOTTA SNACKS FORRA KEEP FIT 'FUN'-ATICS!
SAY THAT AGAIN, BRUVVER?

Answers: 8 Activities BASKETBALL, ROWING, TENNIS, SQUASH, FOOTBALL, BADMINTON, HIKING, JOGGING. Beryl's Quiz 1) BEE 2) BARN 3) BRAKE 4) BRANCH 5) BUTTONS. Gym Words PAY, YEAR, RAGE, EYE, GAVE, GYM, GUM, LOG, YELL, SKY, SEEM, PALM.

DAN/08-04
Gall & Strachan

CUDDLES & DIMPLES
THIS DOESN'T GET MUCH BETTER!
WHASSAT, BRUV?
CAN IT BE?
PLAYING WITH TOY CARS, ON A NICE DAY!
YES, IT IS A NICE DAY.
ER, YEAH.
A VERY, NICE DAY!
IT'S A VERY, VERY NICE DAY!!!
ERK!

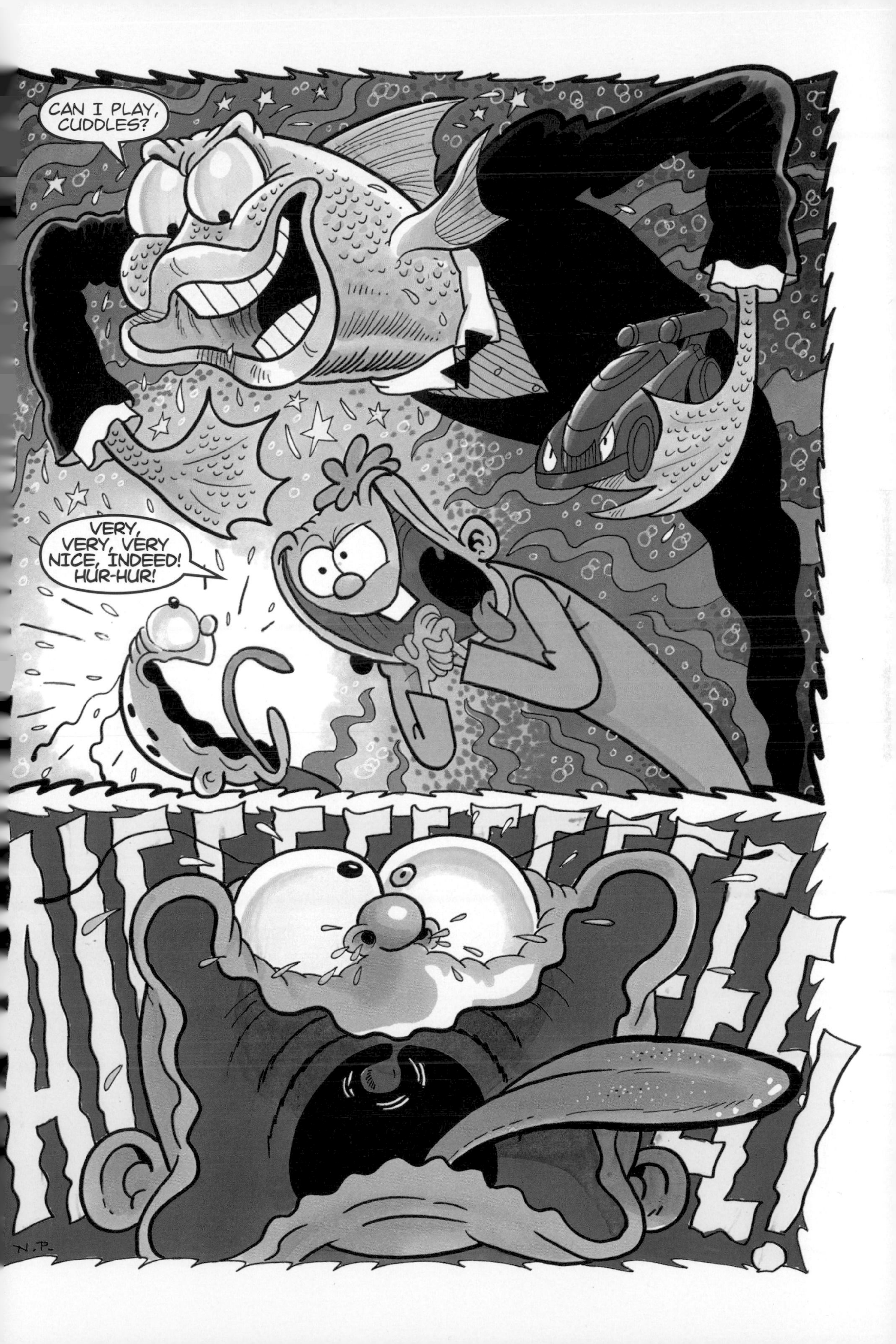
CAN I PLAY, CUDDLES?
VERY, VERY, VERY NICE, INDEED! HUR-HUR!
N.P.

ARGH! FISHY. MONSTER. BAAAD.
NOT THAT DREAM AGAIN.
WIBBLE.
POOR CUDDLES!
YOU OKAY, SON?
Cuddles + Dimples
HE'S DERANGED!
FISH-MONSTER-MAN!
CUDDLES CAN SLEEP IN OUR ROOM.
RESULT! I GET THE ROOM ALL TO MYSELF.
LATER
BLART!
GIRLISH SNORE.

SNORT!
HURMPH.
SHLEP!
GRUNT!
MMM...
Cuddles
+
Dimples
OH, ER, GOOD TO SEE YOU BACK, BRUV!
I'M CURED! AFTER LYING BESIDE DAD, I'M NOT SCARED OF A SILLY FISHY MONSTER ANYMORE!
SADLY, YES.
G'NIGHT!

PINKY'S CRACKPOT CIRCUS
I HEARD THAT A NEWSPAPER REVIEWER IS IN TOWN TONIGHT.
WOW! REALLY?
TICKET OFFICE
BRENDA, KEEP AN EYE OUT FOR THE NEWSPAPER MAN. WE'VE GOT TO MAKE SURE HE'S WELL-TREATED!
OK, PINKY!
TYPICAL PINKY!
ENTRANCE
TICKET OFFICE
PSST! MAYBE IT'S THAT CHAP WITH THE NOTEPAD.
GOOD CALL, BRENDA!
NOW, THERE'S A JOURNALIST OUT THERE. I WANT YOU ALL TO GIVE YOUR BEST PERFORMANCES EVER! REMEMBER, YOU'VE TO MAKE ME, I MEAN, US, LOOK GOOD!
THIS IS THE BEST SEAT IN THE HOUSE, SIR. HOT DOG? FIZZY DRINK?
WHY, THANK YOU! DON'T MIND IF I DO.
FIZZO
LADIES AND JOURNALISTS, I MEAN, GENTLEMEN - PLEASE SHOW YOUR APPRECIATION FOR PINKY'S CRACKPOT CIRCUS! I'M PINKY, BY THE WAY.

BOOM!
BOING!
BLAM!
WE'RE ALL ONE BIG HAPPY FAMILY - AND I'M THE DADDY!

I, PRESUME I - I MEAN, WE, WILL BE GETTING A GOOD REVIEW?
EH? WHAT ARE YOU TALKING ABOUT?
SCRIBBLE!
I'M A UNIVERSITY LECTURER, RESEARCHING OUTDATED ENTERTAINMENT PRACTICES FROM THE LAST CENTURY.
WHAAAAT? WHO YOU CALLING 'OUTDATED'?
FUME! PRETEND TO BE A JOURNALIST, EH?
SPLAT!
TAKE THAT!
STOMP! STOMP! STOMP!
GLUB!
AIIIIEEEE!
BOOM!
RESEARCH THIS, EGGHEAD!
PRESS
BLIMEY, WHAT A SCOOP. I'M GLAD I MISSED MY TRAIN!
NEXT DAY -
WHAT DOES 'DISASTROUS PUBLICITY' MEAN?
DAILY TOOT
CIRCUS TERROR! BIG TOP CRUELTY!
IT MEANS I'M RUINED. SIGH!

BANANAMAN
SUPER-VILLAINS LAIR
THIS WAY
SUPERVILLAINS LAIR—
3rd LEFT
SUPERVILLAINS
SECRET LAIR
2nd RIGHT
Supervillains
Top, Top
Secret Lair

DON'T TELL ANYONE!
DON'T TELL ANYONE!
GOODIES KEEP OUT!
AAAH, THIS IS PERFECT FOR RELAXING AFTER A LONG, HARD DAY OF BEING A CRIMINAL MASTERMIND.
T
BICCIES
SWAG
LOOT
£

ANOTHER DAY OF GETTING YOUR BUTT WHIPPED BY BANANAMAN, YOU MEAN.
WHAT?
WHAT DOES YOUR DIARY SAY? MONDAY - LOST TO BANANAMAN. TUESDAY - LOST TO BANANAMAN. WEDNESDAY - TRIMMED MY NOSE HAIRS THEN LOST TO BANANAMAN...
FRIDAY'S NOSE-HAIR TRIMMING DAY.
SLURP!
T
YOU... LOSER!
??????
SPLUTTER!
SAY THAT AGAIN!
SAY IT AGAIN.
AGAIN!
LOSER!
LOSER!
LOSER!
YEAH?
YEAH?
YEAH?
YEAH?
I SHALL PROVE I'M NOT A LOSER.
PROOOOOOVE IT!
HOW CAMP IS THAT?

DOCTOR GLOOM, HEEL! I SHALL NOW PROVE I AM A BETTER BADDIE THAN EDDIE THE GENT!
MOCKING HAH!
THE GENERAL'S BILL, SIR.
HE STIFFED ME FOR THE DRINKS. THE ROTTER!
BILL
SOON...
I'LL SHOW HOW ROTTEN I AM...
PING!
...BY STEALING CANDY FROM A BABY!
WAAH!
HARRUMPH!
SNATCH!
I CAN DO THAT.
BEAT IT, WEIRDO!
WHOP!

ER... TOUGH BABY.
I'D MOCK YOU BUT YOU'RE NOT WORTH THE EFFORT.
BAD JOKE FACTORY
GLOOM, WE'RE GOING UP IN THE WORLD - WE'RE KNOCKING OVER A SWEET SHOP.
WHY CAN'T I BE A PROPER CROOK? LIKE A LAWYER OR A POLITICIAN?
SWEETS
RIGHT, GIMME ALL YOUR JELLY BABIES IN SMALL, UNMARKED BAGS...
...OR THE SHERBET GETS FIZZY!
LEMON SHERBET BON-BONS
OOPS. SORRY WAS THAT ME? I CAN'T CONTROL THIS GUN, YOU KNOW.
KNOCK!

OH, MOTHER. THIS CAN'T BE GOOD.
LOSER! WITH A CAPITAL LOO!
WAAAAGH-OOF!
WEETS
I CHALLENGE YOU TO A DUEL, A DUEL OF EVIL - A DASTARDLY DUEL!
SLAP!
IF MY TOUGH PALS SEE ME WITH YOU I'LL NEVER LIVE IT DOWN!

HERE IS THE NEWS WITH ME, THE LOVELY FIONA...
...GENERAL BLIGHT AND EDDIE THE GENT ARE CAUSING HAVOC WITH THEIR EVIL DUEL. NO-ONE IS SAFE...
SWIPE
NOT EVEN LOVELY NEWSREADERS - THEY STOLE MY EXPENSIVE OUTFIT!
BANANAMAN, HELP!
FIRST, HOO-HOO-HOO, I CAN SEE HER UNDIES...
...AND SECOND OF ALL, ABOUT FLAMING TIME. HALFWAY THROUGH THE STORY AND I'M ONLY JUST SHOWING UP. I'M THE STAR HERE. I HAVE A CONTRACT AND...
CONTRACT
QUIT MOANING AND GET THIS DOWN YER BEAK.
PLOP!

WHEN LITTLE ERIC EATS A BANANA HE BECOMES BANANAMAN, A SUPERHERO... SORT OF...
ZABBADOOOOM!
LIKE I SAID, I'M THE STAR AND...
GET ON WITH THE HERO-ING, YOU BLUE NINNY.
PECK!
BLIGHT'S UP TO NO GOOD IN HERE.
HE'S NOT MAKING IT TOO RUNNY, IS HE? I DON'T LIKE MY CUSTARD RUNNY.
CUSTARD FACTORY

NOPE! WORSE!
KABOOM!
WHOOSH!
THAT'S WAAAY TOO RUNNY!
BANANA CUSTARD?
NEEDS SUGAR.
BEAT THAT, EDDIE.
OKAY. I WILL.
I NEED AN IDEA.

MMMM...
UMMM...
FINALLY...
I HAVE AN IDEA - AND IT'S HOTTER THAN FIONA!
YOU CAN'T SAY THAT IN THE DANDY ANNUAL.
FLUMP!
SUPERVILLAIN OF THE YEAR AWARDS
PLEASURE TO BE HERE.
AUTOGRAPHS LATER.
FLASH! FLASH! FLASH!

ALL RIGHT, MY LOVES? I'LL READ THIS YEAR'S NOMINATIONS...
...GENERAL BLIGHT...
...AND EDDIE THE GENT.
I'M NOT ON TELLY, AM I?
WELL, I DID ROB THE BANK OF ENGLAND - THEIR TEA TROLLEY, ANYWAY - SNAFFLED ALL THE SARNIES.
WELL, I FILLED THE CROWN WITH TRIFLE BEFORE PARLIAMENT OPENED - AND I TURNED THE THAMES INTO A POT NOODLE...
DUNT!
7 HOURS LATER...
...AND I MADE THE RED ARROWS WRITE RUDE WORDS IN THE SKY, AND LAST WEEK I STOLE ALL THE KNICKER ELASTIC IN THE WORLD...
FINISHED? PLEASE?
AND THE WINNER IS...
ME! ME! ME!
ME! ME! ME!

...GENERAL BLIGHT!
YESSS!
BUMS!
GIMME THE PRIZE THEN I CAN THANK ALL THE PEOPLE WHO HELPED ME - THE VICTIMS MAINLY.
HERE'S THE PRIZE YOU'RE GETTING - THE BRACELETS!
BANANAMAN? BUT THAT WAS SUCH A GOOD DISGUISE - THAT'S NOT LIKE YOU.
CLICK!
CLICK!
IT'S THE NICK FOR YOU, GENERAL.
ISN'T BANANAMAN WONDERFUL?
DON'T CARE! I'M THE WINNER!
IT SHOULD HAVE BEEN ME!
IT'S ENOUGH TO MAKE A HORSE SICK. I'M OUT OF HERE!
STEVE BRIGH

BLINKY
THIS TV GUIDE IS RUBBISH!
DOG
WOW!
GO-KART TRACK -OPENS TODAY!!
I'M OFF TO THE GO-KART TRACK. BYE, MUM!
SHLEP!
GERROFF!
VROOM! VROOM!
A-HA. HERE'S THE PLACE!
KARTING WORLD
MEGAMART
AND HERE ARE THE KARTS. COOL!

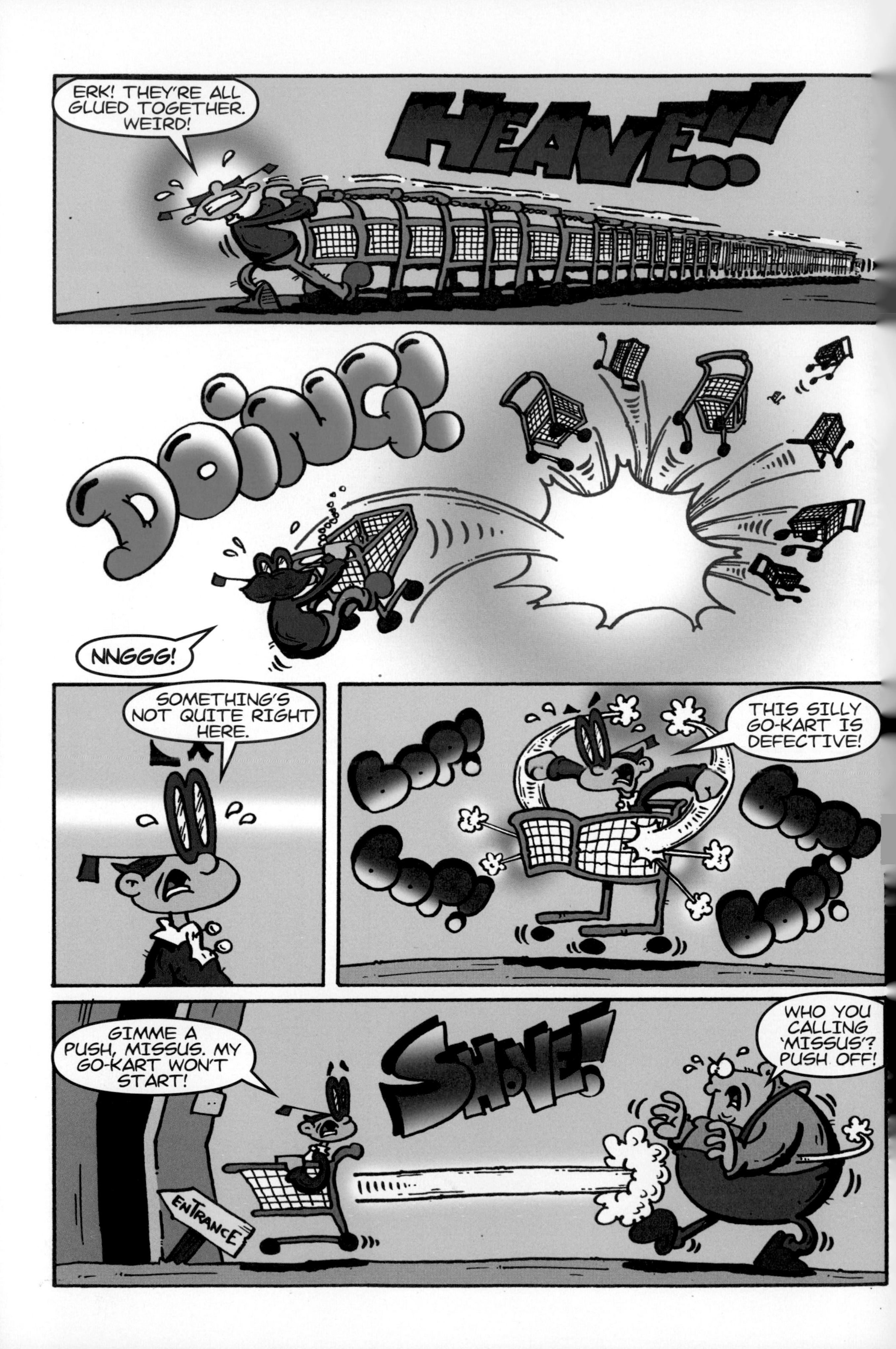
ERK! THEY'RE ALL GLUED TOGETHER. WEIRD!
HEAVE!!
DOING!
NNGGG!
SOMETHING'S NOT QUITE RIGHT HERE.
BOP!
THIS SILLY GO-KART IS DEFECTIVE!
BOP!
BOP!
BOP!
GIMME A PUSH, MISSUS. MY GO-KART WON'T START!
SHOVE!
WHO YOU CALLING 'MISSUS'? PUSH OFF!
ENTRANCE

BOP!
HELP!
SCREAM!
WHIZZ!!!
PRANG!
GROO!
SPLAT!
CUSTARD
ZOOM!
GO-KARTING ROCKS! WHEEEEE!

MANAGER
HALT!
ER, NOT SURE HOW, TO BE HONEST!
WHIZZ!
BLAT!
GET OFF THE RACE TRACK!
UUUUFFF!
OUT, NUTTER!
OOF CITY!
WOOF!
LATER -
BEHIND THE DRIVING WHEEL AT LAST!
HUH! THIS GO-KART WON'T BUDGE EITHER. I GIVE UP!
FUME!
WE WANT A GO!
KARTIE RIDE 20p

HYDE & SHRIEK
YOUNG ERBERT HYDE HAS FALLEN HEIR TO HIS GREAT UNCLE'S CASTLE IN TRANSYLVANIA.
FLIT!
SQUEEK!
I'M BORED, BORED, BORED! THERE'S NOTHING TO DO IN THIS GLOOMY OLD DUMP.
OINK!
HOOF!
YOU'RE MY SERVANT. HAVEN'T YOU GOT ANY TOYS I CAN PLAY WITH?
TOYS, MASTER ERBERT? OF COURSE.
THERE SHOULD BE SOME IN YOUR LATE, GREAT UNCLE JEKYLL'S OLD NURSERY.
OH, GOODY TOOTS!
CHUFFED TO THE SEAMS OF HIS LITTLE FLOWERY Y-FRONTS!

SEE? LOTS OF JOLLY PLAYTHINGS TO KEEP A YOUNG LAD AMUSED FOR HOURS.
G-GULP! THIS WAS TH-THE NURSERY?
BLITHERING WILLIES!
SHOCKING HORSE.
PICKLED GOBLIN EYEBALL
YE IRON SOCK.
WEREWOLF EARWAX
YE DREADED SPIKY Y-FRONTS
MY LITTLE HEARSE.
OGRE SNOT.

AWW! YOUR GREAT UNCLE PLAYED WITH THIS FOR HOURS. THE LITTLE TINKER WAS FOREVER BURYING THINGS.
My Little Undertaker's Set
R.I.P.
YEEEK!
AND LOOK! HIS OLD HEAD-SHRINKING SET.
Junior Head-Shrinking Kit
I'M GOING TO FAINT.
SHUDDER!
HE SO ENJOYED PLAYING WITH HIS LITTLE FRIENDS.
I'LL BET THEY DIDN'T!
UNCLE JEKYLL, AGED TEN.
DIABOLICAL CACKLE!
RUB! RUB!
AND HERE'S HIS VERY FIRST GUILLOTINE.
FREAK-OUT!

FOND MEMORIES!
THE YOUNG SCAMP WOULD ALWAYS WANT THE SERVANTS TO JOIN IN HIS LITTLE GAMES.
YOINKS!
RUMBLE!
COOKY
A TAD WORRIED!
EVIL LEER!
CREAK!
SWEAT!
NERVOUS PAARPLE!
DON'T LOSE YOUR HEAD!
ISN'T TH-THERE ANYTHING LESS SCARY?
WELL...
IN DANGER OF FILLING HIS FRILLIES!
...IF I REMEMBER CORRECTLY YOUR GREAT UNCLE USED TO HAVE A FAVOURITE TEDDY BEAR.
WHOOPEE! THAT'S MORE LIKE IT.
GLEE!
CLUTCH!

I THINK HE USED TO KEEP IT IN THAT CUPBOARD.
I'LL GET IT! I'LL GET IT! I LOVE TEDDY BEARS.
666
PRANCE!
ROAAAAAR!
YES, IT'S STILL THERE.
AAAIIIEEE! HEEEE-ULP!
GRRROWWL!
TIDAL WAVE IN THE TROLLIES!
SNIFF! IT'S NICE TO HEAR THE MERRY SCREAMS OF CHILDISH TERROR AROUND THE OLD PLACE.
GAROOWWWL! RIP! SLASH! SLOBBER! REND! SHRED!
THEN -
MAYBE I'LL FIND SOMETHING NICE IN THIS DUSTY OLD BOX?
!?!
-TOM PATERSON-

IT'S MY SERVANT, MR SHRIEK'S OLD TOY BOX. GOSH!
BLOW!
Master Shriek's Toys
I HATE TO THINK WHAT HORRORS LURK IN THE DARK DEPTHS OF THIS EVIL BOX.
NO! DON'T EVER OPEN THAT.
CREE-EEEAK!
Prepare for thy doom all ye who open this box †
SQUEAKY TEDDIES, FLUFFY BUNNIES, ADORABLE DOLLIES?
ARRGH! MY SECRET SHAME!!
MA-MA!
SWEAT!
Mister Shriek's Toys
HOO-HOO-HOO! I KNEW YOU WERE A SOFTY SOAP SORT OF SILLY VAMPIRE.
I MAY NEVER LIVE THIS DOWN. THOUGH I LIVE ANOTHER FIVE HUNDRED YEARS. SIGH.
HOOT! MOCK! SNORT! POINT!
FLIT!
FLAP!
MINCE!
BLAZIN BEETROOT BLUSH!
ROMP!

BLINKY
SWEETS
MUNCH! MUNCH!
SWEETS
STOP, THIEF! HELP, POLICE!
NOT LIKELY!
SWEETIES
EH?
RIGHT. WHICH WAY DID HE GO? PANT!
THAT WAY. OR WAS IT THIS WAY?
FUME! HE'S ESCAPED!
NICK BRENNAN
I SAW THE WHOLE THING, OCCIFER!
THEN YOU CAN GIVE ME A DESCRIPTION OF THE SUSPECT!
SIGH! ARE YOU SURE THE THIEF LOOKED LIKE THIS?
ERM. ER...
WASTE BIN

•WANTED•
HAVE YOU SEEN THIS MAN?
THE SHIFTY SWEETIE THIEF
ACCORDING TO ONE (UN)RELIABLE WITNESS, SUSPECT IS A 6FT TALL DWARF WITH SHORT (OR POSSIBLY LONG) HAIR; BLUE (OR BROWN) EYES, FAT (OR THIN), AND WEARS A MOUSTACHE (MAYBE) AND SPECTACLES.
L
IF YOU HAVE SEEN THIS MAN, IT'S PROBABLY A MIRACLE.

DREADLOCK HOLMES
A TYPICAL DAY IN DREAD'S SHED -
DREAD'S LITTLE SIS, MARSHA.
KNOCK! KNOCK!
DANDY
THAT'LL BE MUM KNOCKING.
AND -
NO! MUM'S KNOCK IS DIFFERENT. THAT KNOCK WAS FROM A LARGE, BULKY MAN.
RASP! SMARTY-PANTS!
TOLD YOU!
DREADLOCK HOLMES, THE FAMOUS YOUNG DETECTIVE? I NEED YOUR HELP TO SOLVE A MYSTERY!
YEP! THAT'S ME...
...I'LL MEET YOU ROUND THE FRONT!

NOW I'M READY TO INVESTIGATE!
AND -
FOLLOW ME INTO TOWN.
SOMEONE'S BEEN PUTTING THIS ON THE MAYOR'S STATUE EVERY NIGHT!
NOTHING ON THE SECURITY CAMERAS?
NO! ONE MINUTE IT'S CLEAR, THE NEX
IT APPEARS.
MAYBE THE INVISIBLE MAN DID IT?
WHOA! IT'S SLIPPY!
WE'VE TREATED IT WITH PROTECTIVE GREASE TO STOP CLIMBERS.
HMM!
IT COSTS US
A FORTUNE T
BRING IN TH
CHERRY PICKE
EVERY DAY.

IT'S A COMPLETE MYSTERY!
MAYBE NOT...
...FOLLOW ME. THE GAME'S AFOOT!
SO, ON THE 25TH FLOOR -
WHICH OF YOUR EMPLOYEES HAS THE MOST BORING JOB?
THAT'D BE REG.
I DON'T UNDERSTAND!
ME EITHER!
LET'S VISIT REG!
AND -
MYSTERY SOLVED, I THINK! CLOSE THAT WINDOW, REG!
TRYING TO LAND A CONE ON THE MAYOR'S HEAD BRIGHTENS MY DAY!
DON'T DO IT AGAIN!
I'M A GENIUS!
COULDN'T GET A CONE ON YOUR HEAD - IT'S TOO BIG!
STREF

Beryl the Peril
BERYL! TIME TO GET UP!
ZZZZZZZ!
WOSSAT... ? UH...? YUHHH...
YAAAWN! I HATE GETTIN' UP! IN FACT...
...I'M GONNA GO BACK TO BED. ZZZ!
BAH! I'LL HAVE TO GET HER OUTTA BED!
HUP! HUP! HUP! WAKEY-WAKEY!
THUD
YOWPFF!
A QUICK BATH WILL WAKE YOU UP!
WANNA BET?
KNOCK
KNOCK
ZZZZZZZZZ!

HERE'S YOUR... UH? NOT HERE!
BAH! SHE'S BACK IN BED! OH, WELL, MAYBE SHE'D LIKE SOME BREAKFAST!
A GLASS OF MILK...
DONK
YEEEEK! 'S C-C-COLD!
HEH! SHE'S UP!
YURK! SHE'S DOWN! OOF!
SORRY - DAD WON'T BE COMING INTO WORK TODAY. HE ...ER... CAN'T GET OUT OF BED!

CUDDLES and DIMPLES
BABY'S FIRST
QUICK! QUIETLY DOES IT...
SURE, BRUV.
BISCUITS
THERE IT IS. GO GET IT, CUDDLES!
EH?
WHY ME?
BECAUSE I'M THE LOOKOUT!
IT WAS MY GIG. EVERYONE ELSE HAD RUN OUT OF NERVE. EVEN MR BIG.

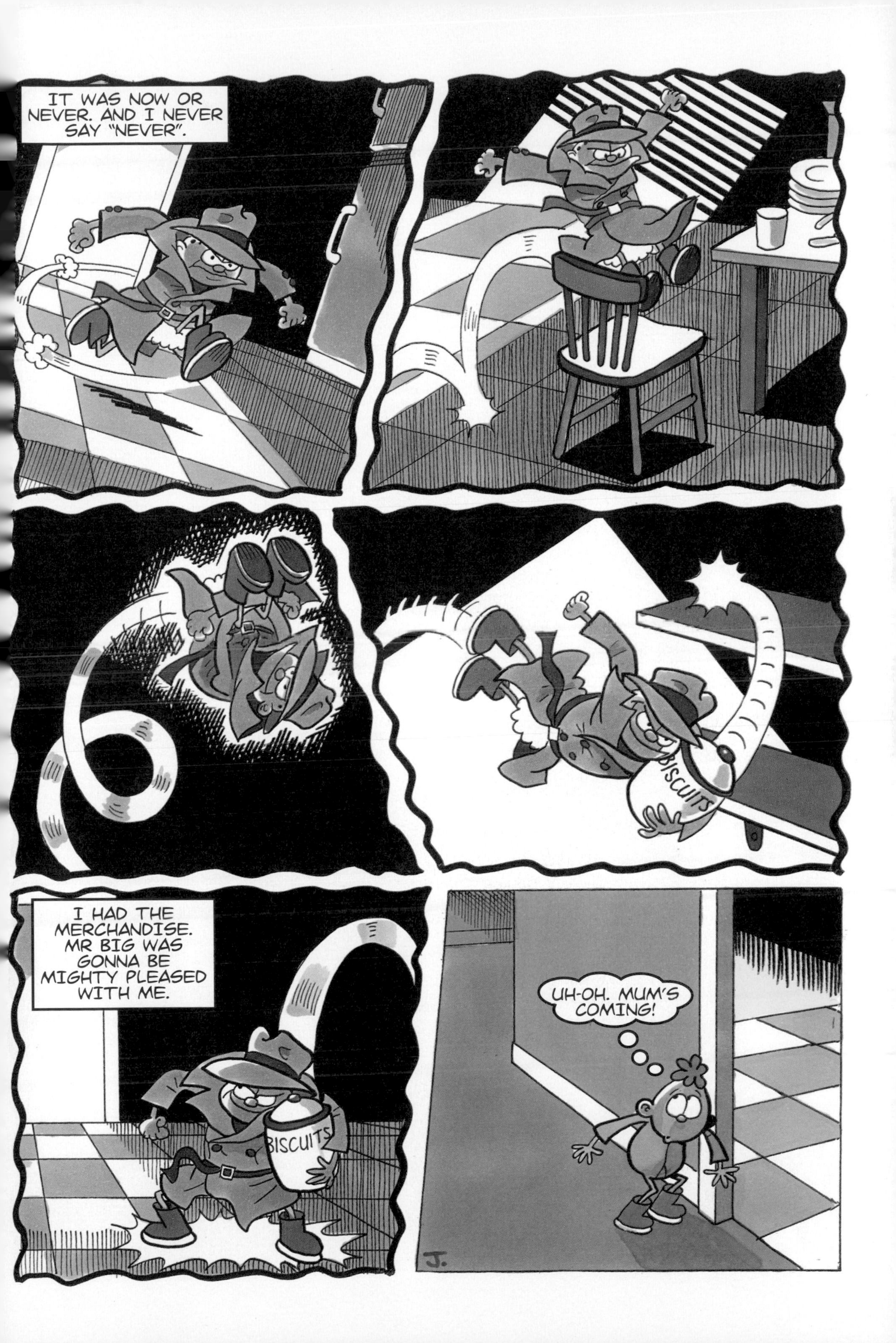
IT WAS NOW OR NEVER. AND I NEVER SAY "NEVER".
BISCUITS
I HAD THE MERCHANDISE. MR BIG WAS GONNA BE MIGHTY PLEASED WITH ME.
BISCUITS
UH-OH. MUM'S COMING!
J.

EVERY TODDLER FOR HIMSELF!
WHAT ARE YOU TWO...
..UP TO? CUDDLES!
BISCUITS
REACH FOR THE SKY, BABYFACE!
THE HEAT! LOOKS LIKE MY LOOKOUT LOOKED OUT ALRIGHT - FOR HIMSELF!
YOU'RE GOING DOWN, BABYFACE. AN' I'M GOING UP - TO SERGEANT!
THE DAME WAS HAVING A GOOD DAY - PITY I WAS PAYING!
MY HANDS WERE REDDER THAN A BABOON'S BUTT.
NAME CUDDLES
11774

THIS WAS GONNA BE A LONG STRETCH.
3FT
2FT
1FT
TWO YEARS? MAN, THAT JUDGE MUST'VE GOT OUT THE WRONG SIDE OF THE BED THIS MORNING!
I'D BEEN INSIDE BEFORE - BUT ONLY FOR NINE MONTHS.
CLANG!
TWO YEARS? I KNEW I COULD NEVER MAKE THAT!
AND YOU'LL STAY THERE UNTIL TEA-TIME!
VISITOR FOR YA, BABYFACE.
I KNEW THE BOYS'D BE IN TOUCH.
I KNEW TOO MUCH FOR THEM TO LEAVE ME ROTTING INSIDE.
HUH. MR BIG SENT HIS DAME INSTEAD OF COMING HIMSELF.
IF THAT BOZO THINKS A BRUNETTE WITH A BIG CAKE CAN TALK BABYFACE ROUND, HE'S GOT ANOTHER THINK COMING!

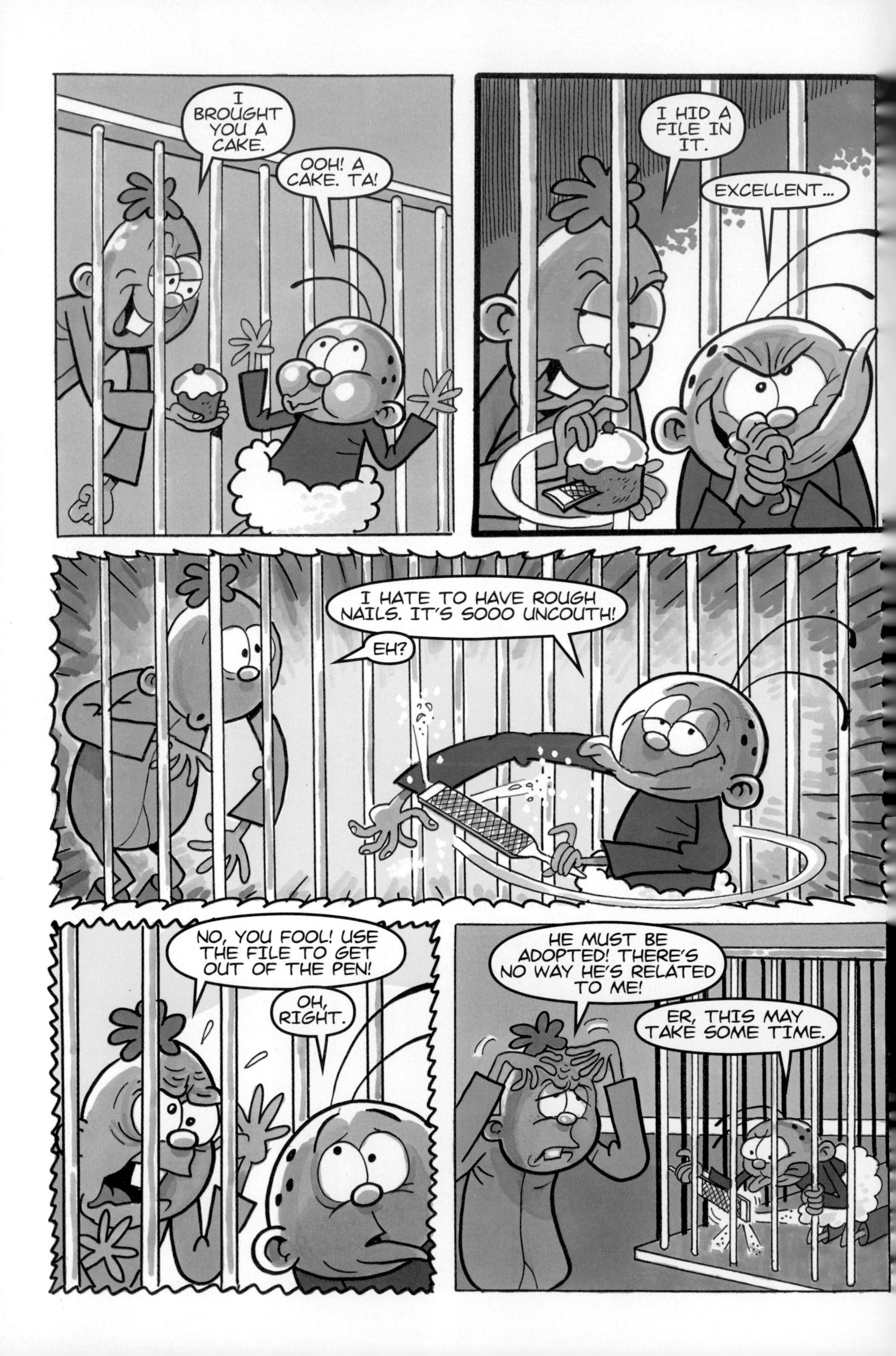
I BROUGHT YOU A CAKE.
OOH! A CAKE. TA!
I HID A FILE IN IT.
EXCELLENT...
I HATE TO HAVE ROUGH NAILS. IT'S SOOO UNCOUTH!
EH?
NO, YOU FOOL! USE THE FILE TO GET OUT OF THE PEN!
OH, RIGHT.
HE MUST BE ADOPTED! THERE'S NO WAY HE'S RELATED TO ME!
ER, THIS MAY TAKE SOME TIME.

I DECIDED TO FORGIVE MR BIG. HE CAME THROUGH BIG STYLE WITH THAT FILE THING.
POLICE
POLICE
IT WAS TIME FOR A SHARP GETAWAY...
...SHARPER THAN A DRAWER FULLA KITCHEN KNIVES.
MR BIG GOT US SOME WHEELS.
PITY I WAS TOO YOUNG TO DRIVE.
THE HEAT WERE IN OUR WAY. AS USUAL.
STOP!
POLICE!
THE HEAT CAN'T HANDLE IT - THEY OUGHTA GET OUTTA THE KITCHEN.
GRRRR!
HURRAH!
HEH-HEH. BABYFACE IS BACK ON THE STREETS!
HURMPH.
THEY ARE IN SOOO MUCH TROUBLE!
PEDAL
PEDAL
NIGEL PARKINSON

YOU'VE HEARD OF SPIELBERG, CAMERON, WOO, EASTWOOD AND HITCHCOCK. WELL, THE DANDY IS PROUD TO BRING YOU THE LATEST DIRECTOR TO JOIN THE LIST OF MOVIE GREATS... BLINKY! WE'LL BE TAKING A LOOK AT SOME OF HIS GREATEST FILMS THROUGHOUT THIS BOOK!

BLINKY'S MAD MOVIES
20th CENTURY TWIT
presents
THE HOUND OF THE BASKERVILLES
starring
BLINKY
as
SHERLOCK HOLMES
I DEDUCE THAT THESE ARE THE FOOTPRINTS OF A GIGANTIC HOUND, WATSON!
ACTUALLY, IT'S MRS DR WATSON'S SLIPPERS, HOLMES.
THE HOUND WORE YOUR WIFE'S SLIPPERS? CUNNING BRUTE!
AND -
BOP!
CHEEKY BLIGHTER!
SPLOOSH!
FIDO
CLANG!!
I DEDUCE THAT THESE ARE THE TOOTHMARKS A GIGANTIC HOUND - AND WISH HE'D LET GO!
Fin
NICK BRENNAN

BRAAAP!
WHAT'S THAT NOISE?
BRAAAAAP!
IT'S GETTING LOUDER!
NYOWWW!
BAD MAX
COOL!
UNCOOL!
I'LL TURN THIS 'SHOPPING TROLLEY' INTO A CHOPPER WORTHY OF THE NAME BAD MAX!

WHAT'S MAX UP TO?
I DON'T KNOW AND I DON'T WANT TO FIND OUT!
CLANG!
BASH!
WHACK!
CLUNK!
NEXT MORNING -
IT'S READY! THE FINEST CHOPPER IN THE WORLD!
IS THE WORLD READY FOR THIS?
AND -
WOW! THAT'S A LOUD BIKE!
BRAAPP!!
THAT'S WHAT TEN-CARD POWER SOUNDS LIKE!
WOW! IT MUST REALLY SHIFT!
IT DOES. MIND YOU DON'T GET BLOWN AWAY WHEN I OPEN HER UP!

GO ON, THEN. LET IT RIP.
SIGH!
HAW-HAW!
MAX EMBARRASSMEN
PEDAL.... PEDAL..... PEDAL..... PEDAL......
BRAAAP!
NYOWWWW!
AHA! I HEAR MY TICKET TO MAX VELOCITY COMING...
...LIGHT-SPEED, HERE I COME!
WHOOOSH!
GET YOUR MOTOR RUNNING...

VAAROOOM!
...HEAD OUT ON THE HIGHWAY!
HEY! WHY ARE YOU SLOWING DOWN?
OH!
MAX TREPIDATION!
S-N-A-P!
COTTON WOOL FACTORY
MAX RELIEF!
A NICE, SOFT LANDING!

VROOOOOM!
KERASH!
New Management
GRISLEY's BARBED WIRE MANUFACTORY
OO! POOR LADDIE!
WAAAAHHH
YEOOOW
OOAAARREE
AFTER MY LITTLE ACCIDENT, I'M FINDING IT DIFFICULT TO KEEP MY BALANCE.
TITTER!
MAX HUMILIATION!
TRUNDLE!
RATTLE!

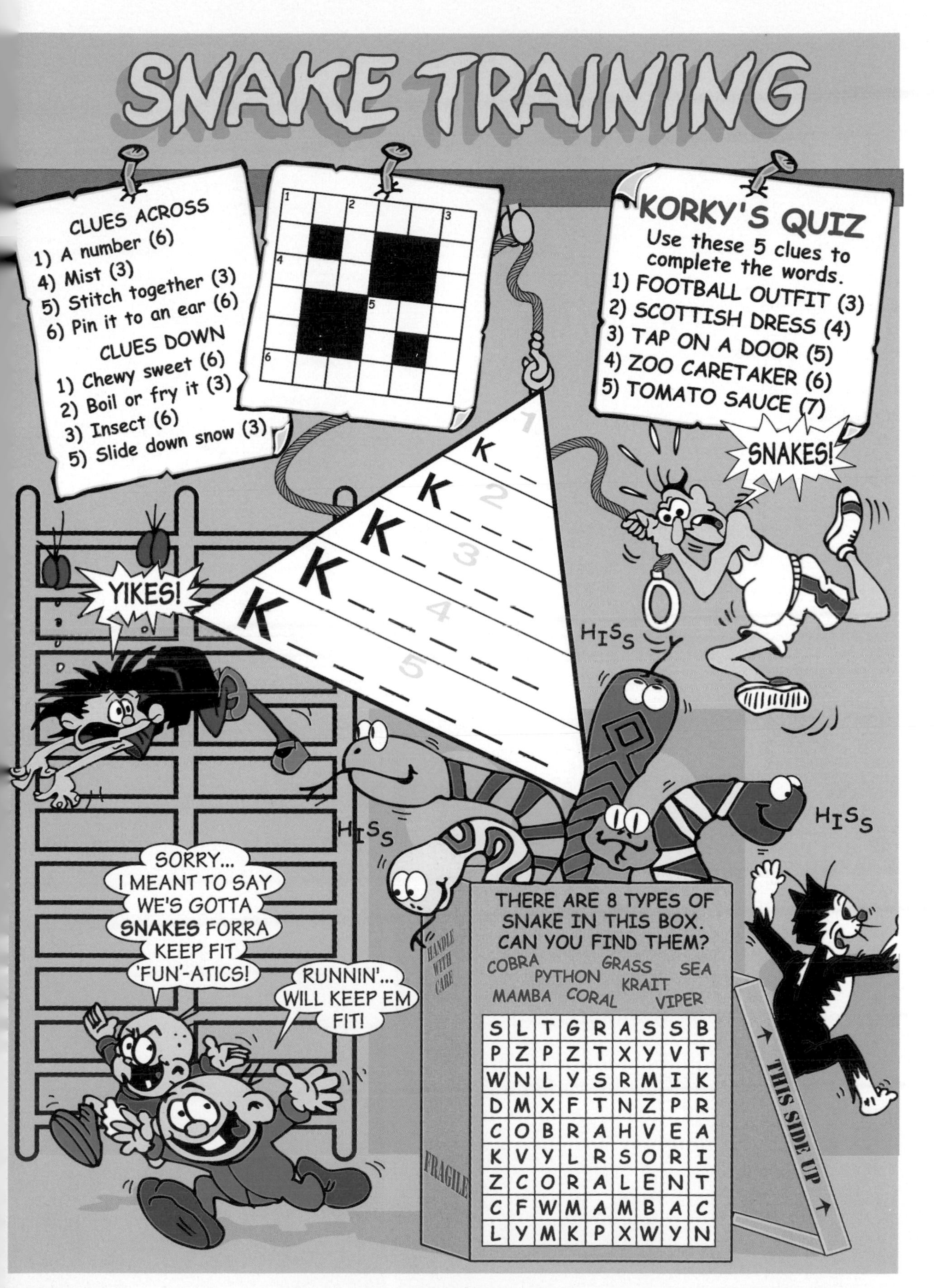

SNAKE TRAINING
CLUES ACROSS
1) A number (6)
4) Mist (3)
5) Stitch together (3)
6) Pin it to an ear (6)
CLUES DOWN
1) Chewy sweet (6)
2) Boil or fry it (3)
3) Insect (6)
5) Slide down snow (3)
KORKY'S QUIZ
Use these 5 clues to complete the words.
1) FOOTBALL OUTFIT (3)
2) SCOTTISH DRESS (4)
3) TAP ON A DOOR (5)
4) ZOO CARETAKER (6)
5) TOMATO SAUCE (7)
SNAKES!
YIKES!
HISS
HISS
HISS
SORRY... I MEANT TO SAY WE'S GOTTA SNAKES FORRA KEEP FIT 'FUN'-ATICS!
RUNNIN'... WILL KEEP EM FIT!
THERE ARE 8 TYPES OF SNAKE IN THIS BOX. CAN YOU FIND THEM?
COBRA PYTHON GRASS KRAIT SEA MAMBA CORAL VIPER
S L T G R A S S B
P Z P Z T X Y V T
W N L Y S R M I K
D M X F T N Z P R
C O B R A H V E A
K V Y L R S O R I
Z C O R A L E N T
C F W M A M B A C
L Y M K P X W Y N
HANDLE WITH CARE
FRAGILE
THIS SIDE UP

Answers: Crossword Across 1)TWELVE 4) FOG 5) SEW 6) EARING. Down 1) TOFFEE 2) EGG 3) EARWIG 5) SKI. Korky's Quiz 1) KIT 2) KILT 3)KNOCK 4) KEEPER 5) KETCHUP.

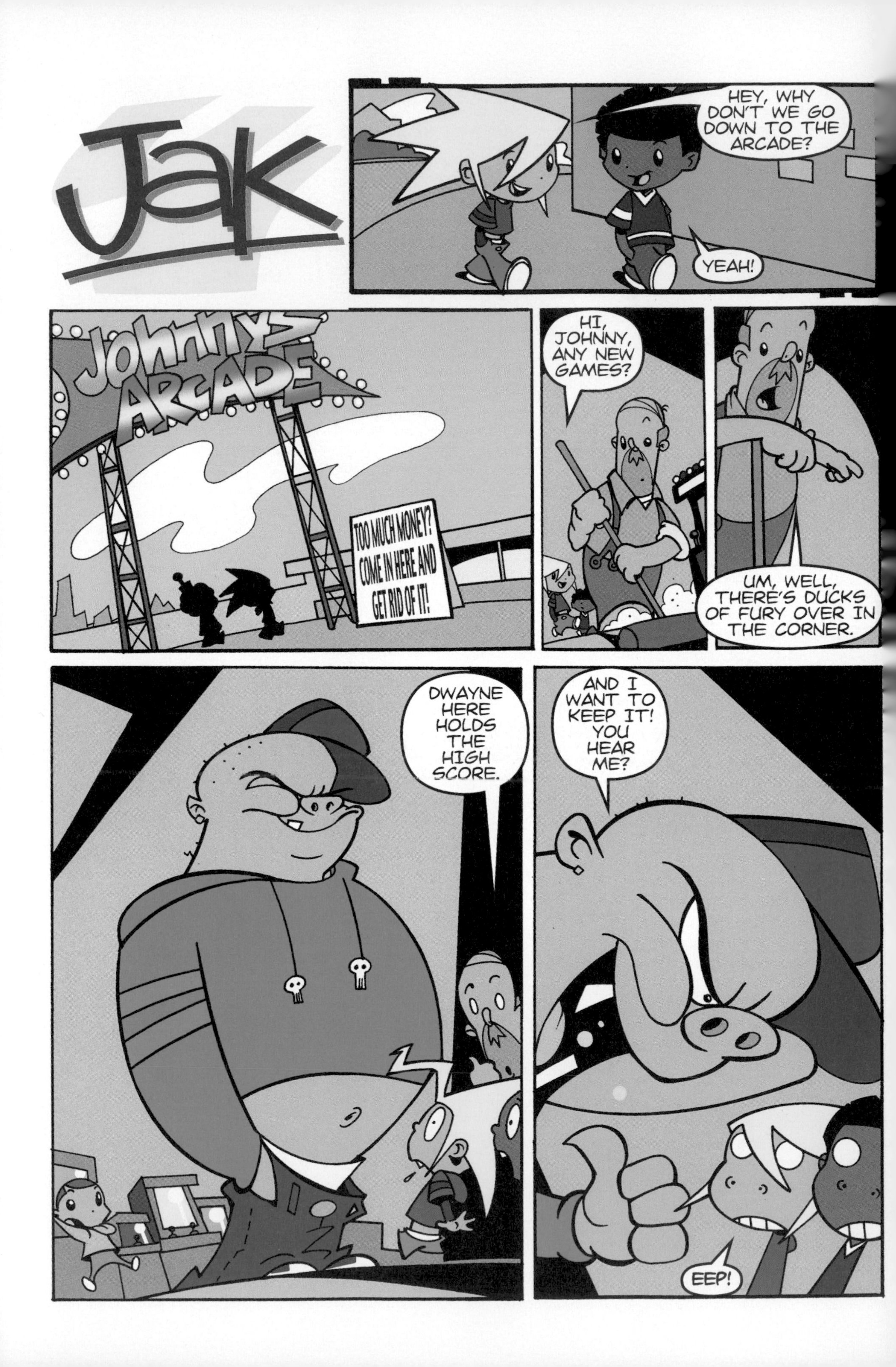
JAK
HEY, WHY DON'T WE GO DOWN TO THE ARCADE?
YEAH!
JOHNNY'S ARCADE
TOO MUCH MONEY? COME IN HERE AND GET RID OF IT!
HI, JOHNNY, ANY NEW GAMES?
UM, WELL, THERE'S DUCKS OF FURY OVER IN THE CORNER.
DWAYNE HERE HOLDS THE HIGH SCORE.
AND I WANT TO KEEP IT! YOU HEAR ME?
EEP!

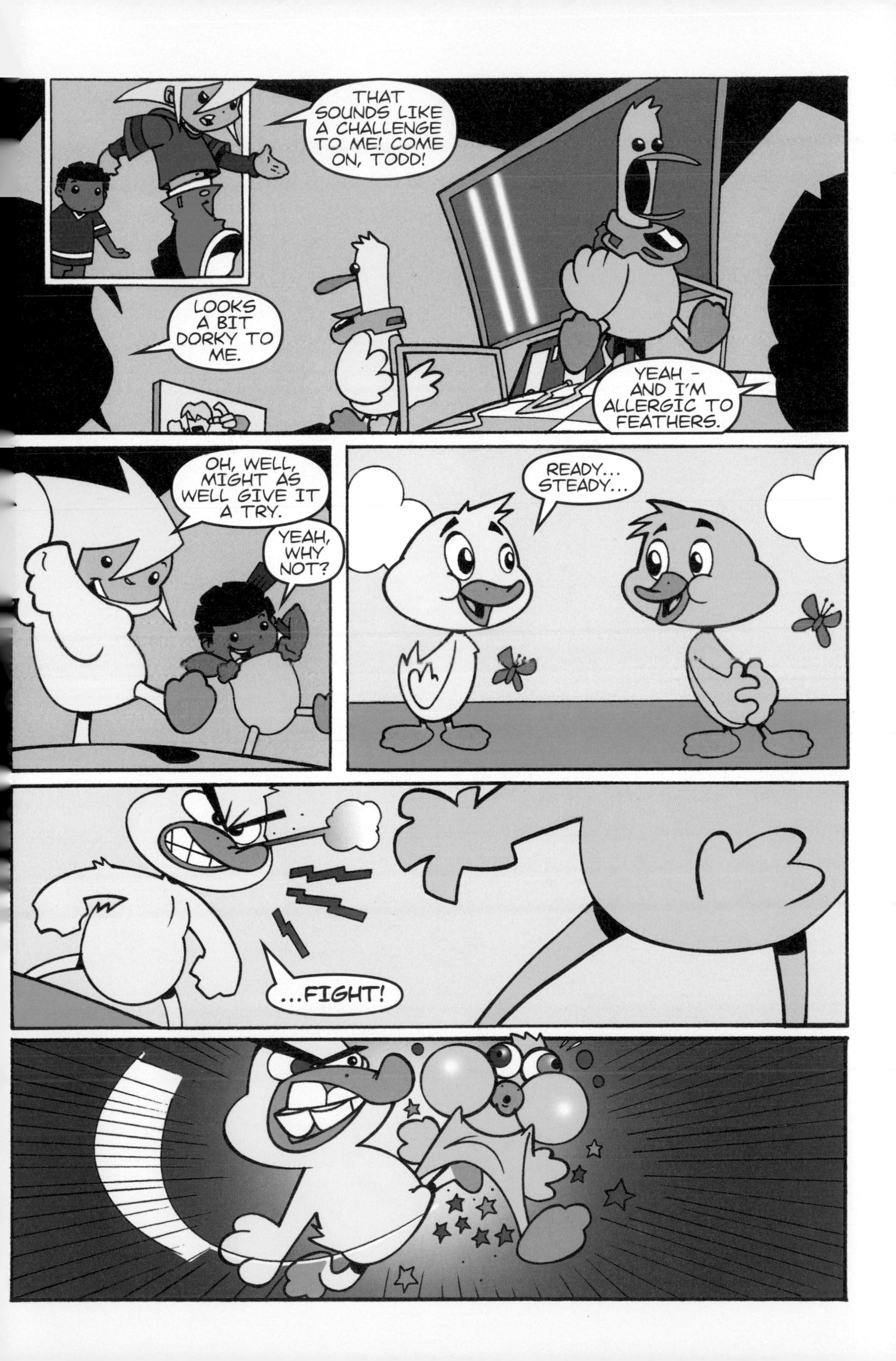
THAT SOUNDS LIKE A CHALLENGE TO ME! COME ON, TODD!
LOOKS A BIT DORKY TO ME.
YEAH - AND I'M ALLERGIC TO FEATHERS.
OH, WELL, MIGHT AS WELL GIVE IT A TRY.
YEAH, WHY NOT?
READY... STEADY...
...FIGHT!

OW!
OOH!
EH? WHAT GIVES?
WHOOPS! DID I DO THAT? SO SORRY - NOT!

YOU BIG DORK! GET INTO THE OTHER SUIT AND GET READY TO TAKE A BEATING!
YOU'LL BE SPITTING FEATHERS FOR WEEKS, BOY!
OH YEAH? WE'LL SEE!
WHAT ARE YOU DOING?
I'M NOT GOING TO FIGHT HIM! ONCE I BEAT HIM, HE'LL PULVERISE ME!
C'MON, DWEEB! WHERE ARE YOU?
KISS IT! KISS IT!
LIKE IT'S YOUR GRANNY'S CHEEK!
GRRR!
GRAAAAHH!

LET'S GET OUT OF HERE!
RIGHT BEHIND YOU!
GRAAHHH!
EEP!
RIGHT AHEAD OF YOU NOW!
SPLIT!
WHERE DID THEY GO?
GRAAAH!

EH?
GERROFF!
DUCKY-WUCKY!
GRR! JUST WAIT, DWEEBS!
MUMMY TAKE YOUR PICTURE WITH THE CUTE DUCKY-WUCKY!
YEAH, YOU'RE SO CUTE, DWAYNE!
LUCKY DUCKY-WUCKY!
WAYNE · THOMPSON ·

BLINKY'S MAD MOVIES
20th CENTURY VOLE
presents
KING KONG
starring BLINKY as KONG
(no, really)
THERE'S A TERRIFYING GORILLA IN THS FILM, SO I'VE BEEN TAKING SPECIAL LESSONS.
WILL WE START NOW OR WILL WE HAVE A...
...COFFEE!
HAVE I UPSET YOU MISS TWATTS?
NO, BUT IT'S TIME YOU GOT INTO...
...COSTUME!
???
IT WAS SCREAMING LESSONS.
I'M SHORT-SIGHTED, LADY - NOT DEAF!
NICK BRENNAN
FIN

WINKER WATSON
WELCOME BACK TO BOGMUIR SCHOOL, WHERE THE WEATHER HAS TURNED ...SCOTTISH.
ATISHMOOO!
WHICH MEANS WINKER AND HIS MATES ARE STUCK IN MCCREEP'S CLASSROOM.
THIS TRIP IS MEGA BORING, WINKER.
NOT FOR CREEP AND SNYDE. THEY'RE UPSTAIRS ADMIRING THE LOCAL MOTHS.
I WANT YOU NOW TO READ UP ON SCOTTISH MYTHS AND CUSTOMS.
MUST WE.
HA! SCOTS CALL SCARECROWS TATTIE BOGLES.
DON'T YOU FIND THOSE ON A HANKIE?
FINISHED THE BOOK, SIR.
THEN YOU MAY WATCH SOME TV THEN.
HEY! THE FIRST TREAT IN TEN YEARS.
BUT YOU CAN ONLY WATCH THE NEWS. I'VE NOT GONE SOFT.
MIGHT'VE KNOWN!
HOLD ON - SOME AMERICAN HUNTERS ARE IN THIS AREA LOOKING FOR THE LOCH NESS MONSTER.

I'LL CATCH THE MONSTER OR MY NAME AIN'T AXEL LEGG.
I'VE HEARD ENOUGH. ALL MEET AT MID-NIGHT. THIS IS THE BIG ONE.
SO, AT MIDNIGHT -
MR. CREEP'S ASLEEP. NOW WE GO AND FIND THE MONSTER HUNTERS.
ZZZZZZ!
SOON -
THERE'S THEIR CAMP. FOLLOW ME, CO-WANGLERS.
MR. LEGG! CAN WE JOIN YOU?
COME ON DOWN, GUYS. BET YOU WANT TO KNOW HOW WE'RE GONNA CATCH THAT OL' MONSTER.
NAH! WE'RE HERE TO TELL YOU THAT NESSIE'S NOT EVEN IN SCOTLAND ANY MORE.
SHE RETIRED TO THE BAHAMAS YEARS AGO.
YOU WANT TO BE AFTER THE TATTIE BOGLES THAT HAUNT THESE HILLS.
I DO? WHAT ARE THEY?

THEY'RE THIN, NASTY CREATURES, DRESSED IN RAGS.
LIKE SCARECROWS THAT HAVE COME ALIVE.
HEAR THAT, MEN? THIS COULD BE BIGGER THAN THE YETI.
LET'S GET ON ITS TRAIL.
LATER AT BOGMUIR.
COME ON, WE'VE GOT A HIKE PLANNED FOR TODAY.
CAN'T GO, SIR. WE'VE ALL GOT TUMMY ACHE.
COME ALONG THEN, TEACHERS. WE'RE NOT WASTING A LOVELY DAY LIKE THIS.
THEY DON'T KNOW I MADE CHANGES TO THEIR MAP LAST NIGHT.
SOON -
EEEK!
THERE'S NO FENCE ON MY MAP - BUT OVER YOU COME, MISS SNYDE.
HA! HA! LOOK AT THE STATE OF THEM - THEIR CLOBBER'S SHREDDED.
AND THAT'S FOR STARTERS.
THIS IS AWFUL! WE'RE BEING TORN TO PIECES.
THE THORN PATCH ISN'T ON THE MAP.
OO-CHA! THISTLES NOW. THAT HAS GOT TO HURT.
YEAH, THEY LOOK JUST LIKE SCARECROWS ... WHICH MEANS IT'S TIME TO MAKE A CALL ...

MR. LEGG? TATTIE BOGLES SPOTTED IN THE GLEN.
AND -
GEE, GUYS - THEY'RE HIDEOUS CREATURES.
WE'LL NET 'EM.
WAIL!
THEY'RE STRUGGLING, ZAK. PACIFY 'EM!
RESULT!
SETTLE DOWN, YOU UGLY CRITTERS!
THWACK!
WILL WE TAKE 'EM TO THE ZOO, AXEL?
I'LL MAYBE STUFF THE BIG ONE.
AT BOGMUIR -
YOU ARE THE FINEST WANGLER, WINKER.
AGREED! SO LET'S PARTY.

THIS IS THE LIFE! NO TEACHERS AROUND AT ALL.
MAYBE THEY'LL NEVER COME BACK.
BUT -
OH, THE PAIN! WATSON LANDED US INTO TERRIBLE TROUBLE THEN.
I'LL DEAL WITH HIM.
NO, I WILL, COUSIN! YOU'RE TOO SOFT!
UH-OH!
AS A PUNISHMENT YOU LOT WILL GET YOURSELVES INTO BOGMUIR LOCH FOR A SWIM.
DON'T SOUND SO BAD.
BOGMUIR LOCH IS ONLY ONE DEGREE ABOVE FREEZING EVEN IN THE SUMMER.
I CAN'T FEEL MY TOES!
GASP!
NOW GET TO BED EARLY. IT'S THE SCHOOL HIGHLAND DAY TOMORROW.
BRRR!

NEXT DAY -
WHAT DO WE DO ON THIS HIGHLAND DAY, ARCHIE?
REALLY TOUGH SPORTS, THAT'S WHAT.
HERE ARE THE SCHOOL BOARD. SO BEST BEHAVIOUR - OR ELSE!
WELCOME TO TOSSING THE CABER, GUYS.
EASY-PEASY OLD SCOTTISH SPORT.
HIGHLAND COW RIDING NEXT! HA! HA!
EEK!
NOW UPHILL SKIING. PANT!
THIS ISN'T SPORT, IT'S TORTURE, WINKER.
LUNCHTIME! TURNIP SANDWICHES FOR ALL BOYS - IN THE CANTEEN.
WHAT'S THIS ON THE WALL, ARCHIE?
IT'S AN OLD SCHOOL PHOTO FROM 1902.
Class of 1902
McCREEP MINOR
HOLD ON - THERE'S MCCREEP. HE MUST BE OVER A HUNDRED YEARS OLD.
HE SHOULD HAVE RETIRED YEARS AGO.

FETCH ME A FISHING ROD, ARCHIE.
ON IT, WINKER.
AHA!
HEY! YOU'RE ANCIENT, MCCREEP - AWAY AND GET YOUR PENSION, MAN.
THAT LOOKS LIKE MY OLD UNCLE ALBERT DOWN THERE - HE WAS A BALD EAGLE.
COME ON, FELLAH. BACK TO THE OLD FOLKS NEST WITH YOU.
PUT ME DOWN, YOU OVERGROWN BUDGIE!
WE NEED A REPLACEMENT. LUCKILY MY NIECE HAS JUST FINISHED TEACHER TRAINING.
HELLO, BOYS.
SIGH!
WE'LL HAVE CAKES TO CELEBRATE.
I THINK BOGMUIR HAS JUST GOT LOTS, LOTS BETTER.
WE'RE ALL READY TO GO BACK SOUTH, ARCHIE. IT WAS GREAT TO MEET YOU, MATE.
I'VE GOT YOU A WEE SOUVENIR.
WICKED! I'LL PUT THEM TO GOOD USE.
NEVER STOP WANGLING, WINKER.

STOP DILLY-DALLYING, BOY! SEE TO THE CASES!
YES, MR. CREEP.
THAT NIGHT -
HOME SWEET HOME BACK AT GREYTOWERS. OFF YOU LOT GO NOW!
WE'LL GET UNPACKED THEN SURPRISE THEM WITH A MATHS TEST.
THAT'S WHAT YOU THINK, CREEPO.
AAARRGH! IT'S THESE HORRIBLE HAGGISES!
THAT'S WHAT ARCHIE GAVE ME, TROTTY.
THEY SEEM TO LIKE YOU, SIR!
MAUL
NIP
SNAP
GET THEM OFF!
WHAT'S THE MEANING OF THIS, MR. CREEP. GET THESE BEASTS ROUNDED UP AT ONCE.
Y-YES, HEADMASTER!
I WISH WE'D NEVER SET EYES ON SCOTLAND, MISS SNYDE.
HA! HA! I DON'T THINK THERE WILL BE ANY MATHS TEST, GUYS.
SW05'

BLINKY'S MAD MOVIES
20th CENTURY FERRET
presents
TARZAN
starring BLINKY as TARZAN
ME TARZAN, YOU JANE!
I'M OVER HERE, PLONKER!
AND YOU THROW YOUR VOICE TOO. SUCH TALENT!
SWING!
CLUB!
I DO APOLOGISE. SOMETHING I ATE DISAGREEING WITH ME.
AAAA-EEE-AAAAH!
SKIP!
C'MON. YOU'RE MORE FUN THAN LION. FANCY A BANANA?
RATHER HAVE A CURRY.
FIN
NICK BRENNAN

BUT WHY DO I HAVE TO PEEL ALL THE POTATOES?
YOU JUST DO, CORPORAL!
CORPORAL CLOTT
BUT I'M A LEAN, MEAN FIGHTING MACHINE!
THERE'S A STAIN ON YOUR APRON, CORPORAL!
OH, THE SHAME!
SIGH, THIS IS SO BORING!
I KNOW HOW TO GET OUT OF THIS!
OKAY IF WE HAVE MASHED POTATOES TONIGHT, SIR?
YES, YES, WHATEVER...
EXCELLEN

I'M DESPERATE FOR THE BATHROOM!
I'LL NIP BEHIND THOSE BUSHES. IT'LL SAVE MOPPING OUT THE TANK LATER.
PERFECT!

AND -
THAT'S BETTER...

OH, NO!
NO TANK!

WHAT'S THAT? HOLD ON, I CAN'T HEAR YOU!
VROOOM! VROOOM! VROOOM!

KEEP THAT DIN DOWN! I'M ON THE PHONE!
SORRY, SIR!
YOU LOST IT? HOW COULD YOU LOSE A TWENTY-TON TANK? FIND IT AGAIN, OR YOU'LL PAY FOR IT!
THIS IS MUCH EASIER THAN PEELING ALL THOSE SPUDS!
FORWARD
REVERSE
I THOUGHT I TOLD YOU TO CUT THE... CLOTT!
VROOOOOM! TRUNDLE! MASH!
HELP! IT'S THE GENERAL! I'VE GOT TO GET OUT OF HERE!

THEN -
HELP!
SHLERRRRP!
VROOOM!
EEK! WHAT WILL I DO?
CLOTT! THIS IS YOUR FAULT!
ULP!
I'LL HIDE IN HERE!
GLOOP!
EH? IT'S NOT TEA-TIME YET. WHAT'S GOING ON?
SCOOP! SCOOP!
CHEW! GUZZLE!
CHOMP!
SCOOP SCOOP
GUZZLE!
GULP!
KEEP EATING, MEN! WE'LL SCOFF THE CHUMP OUT OF HIDING!
NOSH! NOSH!
MOTHER!
STEVE BRIGHT

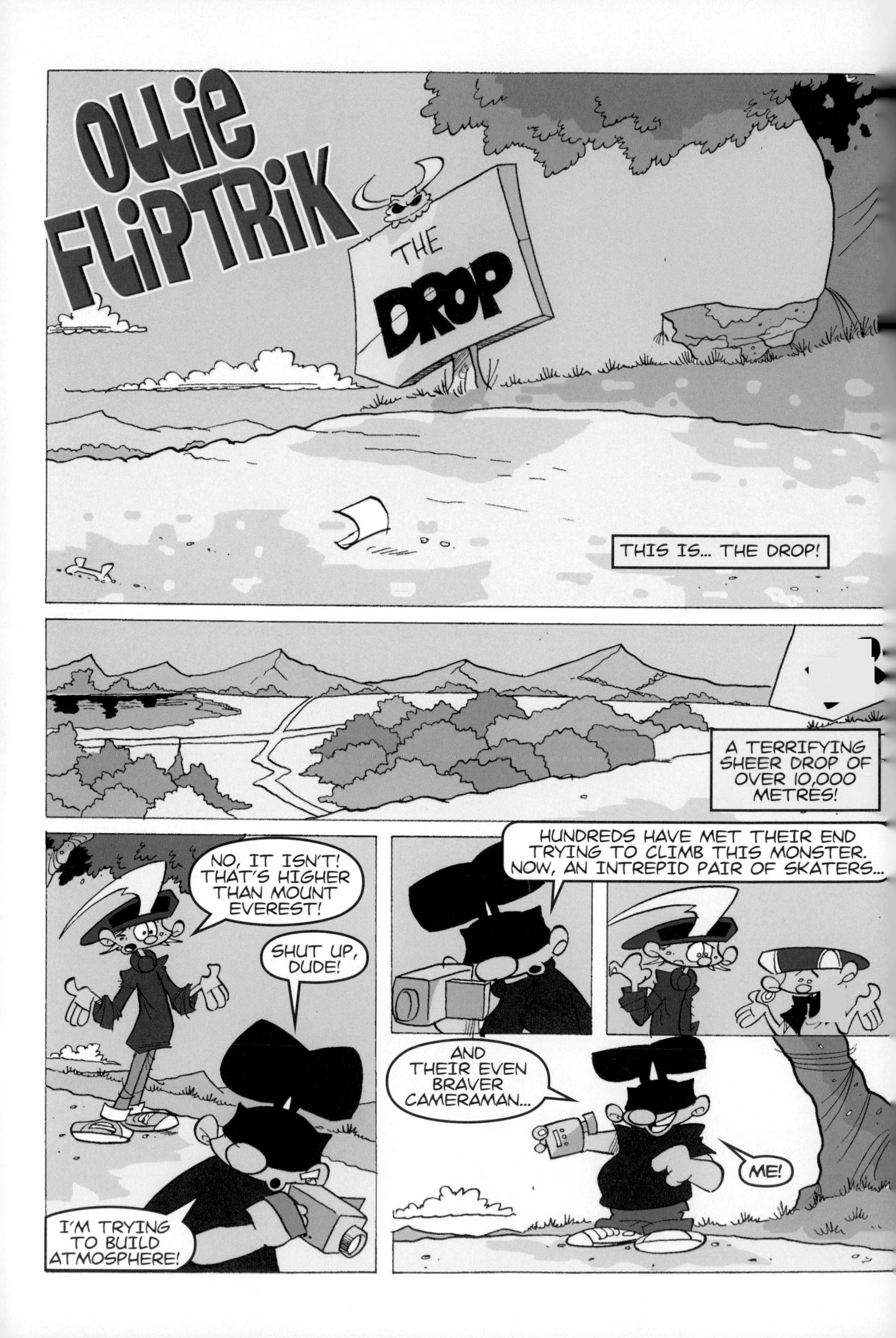
OLLIE FLIPTRIK
THE DROP
THIS IS... THE DROP!
A TERRIFYING SHEER DROP OF OVER 10,000 METRES!
NO, IT ISN'T! THAT'S HIGHER THAN MOUNT EVEREST!
SHUT UP, DUDE!
I'M TRYING TO BUILD ATMOSPHERE!
HUNDREDS HAVE MET THEIR END TRYING TO CLIMB THIS MONSTER. NOW, AN INTREPID PAIR OF SKATERS...
AND THEIR EVEN BRAVER CAMERAMAN...
ME!

... ARE GOING DOWN IT ON SKATEBOARDS. ARE WE MAD? SUPER-BRAVE? OR MAD?
YOU ALREADY SAID 'MAD'.
GET A MOVE ON, OR I'LL TAKE MY CAMERA BACK!
WHEN I GET THAT OSCAR, I WON'T EVEN MENTION YOU IN MY SPEECH.
READY?
READY!
ACTION!
GERONIMO-O-O!
THE DROP
ALREADY DOING 250MPH, THE GUYS APPROACH THE FIRST BEND...
THEY MADE IT!
MOOO
ZOOOOOO

ULP! BUT I DON'T THINK I WILL!
OW!
OOOOCH!
HMMM... I'VE STOPPED, BUT THE WORLD SEEMS TO BE AT AN ODD ANGLE.
THAT WAS SORE!
EEK! OBSTRUCTION IN THE ROAD!
!?!
LOOK OUT!

YEEE-
OWWW! THIS IS GONNA HURT WHEN THE TCP GOES ON!
OH.
WELL?
DID YOU GET IT?
YUP, IT'S ALL HERE...
REMIND ME - WHAT BUTTON WAS 'RECORD' AGAIN?
TWIT!
POW
HEY! IT WAS AN ACCIDENT!
BIFF
SOK
HEH! THAT'S ONE FILM YOU DON'T WANT TO SEE, READERS!

ONE OF MY MILLIONS OF FANS WANTS TO KNOW WHAT I LOOK LIKE UNDER MY MASK.
BANANAMAN
THAT, MY FRIENDS, IS THE WORLD'S MOST SECRET SECRET!
EVEN I HAVEN'T LOOKED!
SO WHEN SOMEONE TRIES TO UNMASK ME, I DON'T LIKE IT. NOT ONE LITTLE BIT...

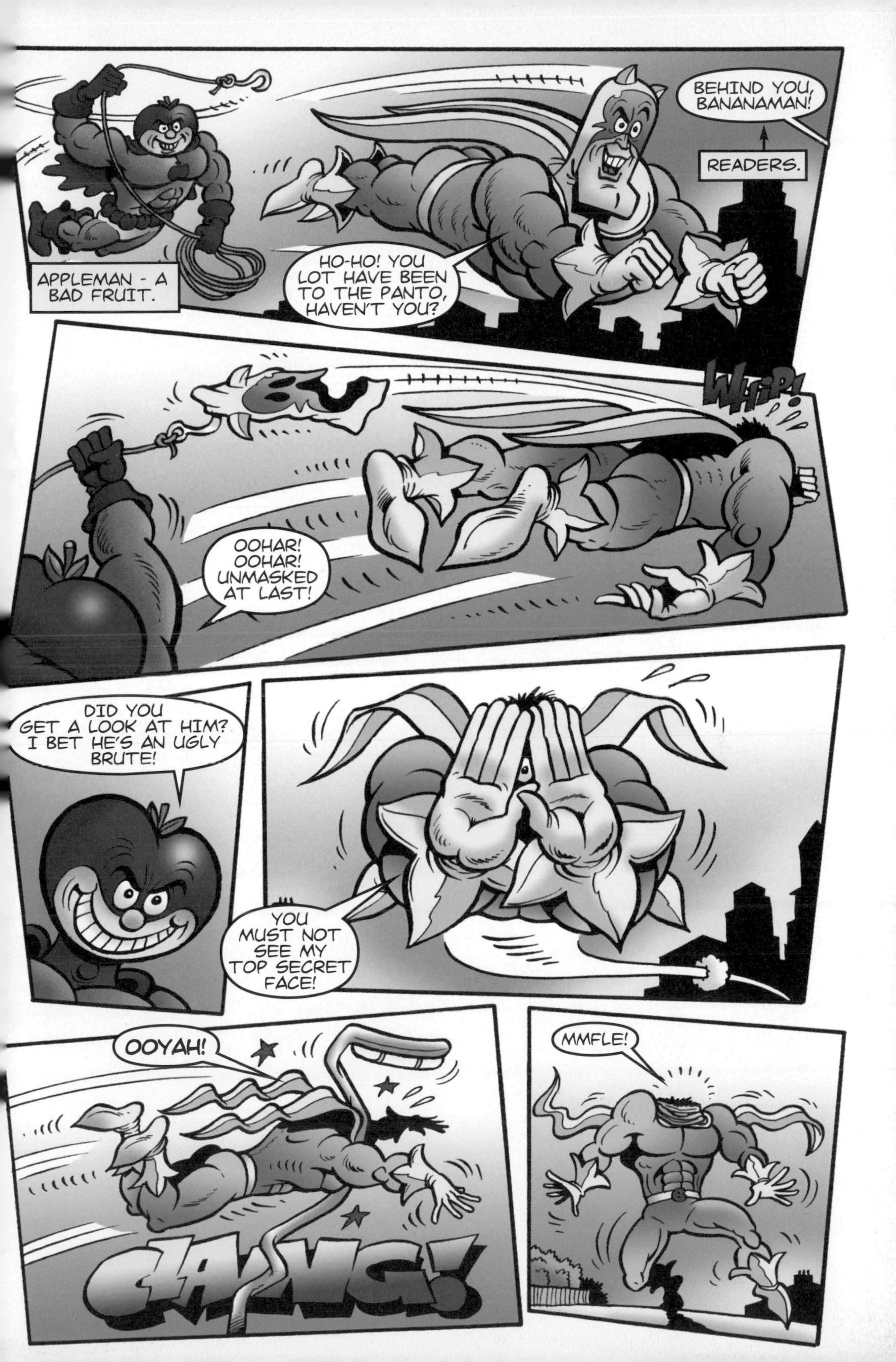
APPLEMAN - A BAD FRUIT.
HO-HO! YOU LOT HAVE BEEN TO THE PANTO, HAVEN'T YOU?
READERS.
BEHIND YOU, BANANAMAN!
WHIP!
OOHAR! OOHAR! UNMASKED AT LAST!
DID YOU GET A LOOK AT HIM? I BET HE'S AN UGLY BRUTE!
YOU MUST NOT SEE MY TOP SECRET FACE!
OOYAH!
CLANG!
MMFLE!

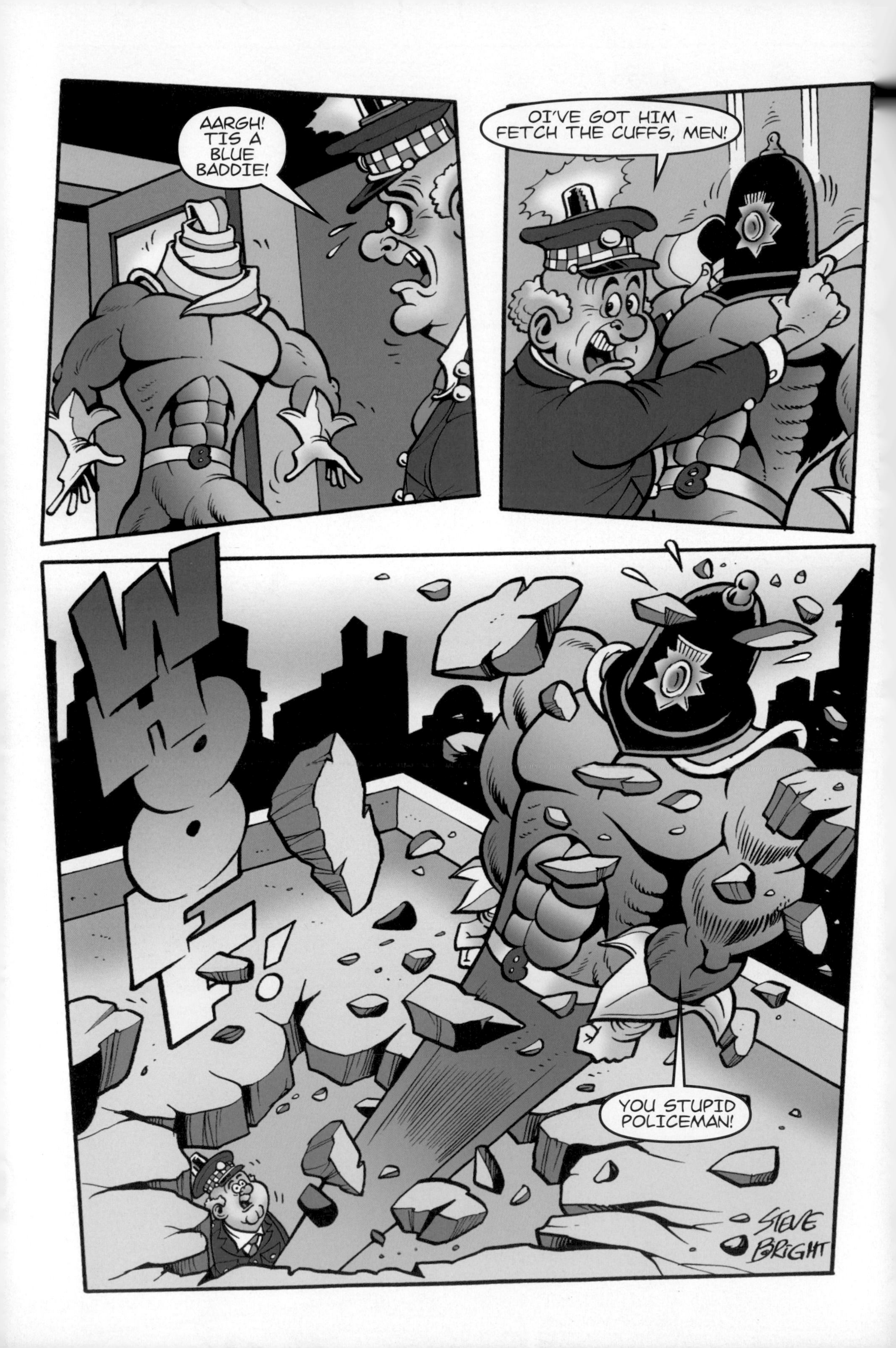
AARGH! TIS A BLUE BADDIE!
OI'VE GOT HIM - FETCH THE CUFFS, MEN!
WHOOF!
YOU STUPID POLICEMAN!
STEVE BRIGHT

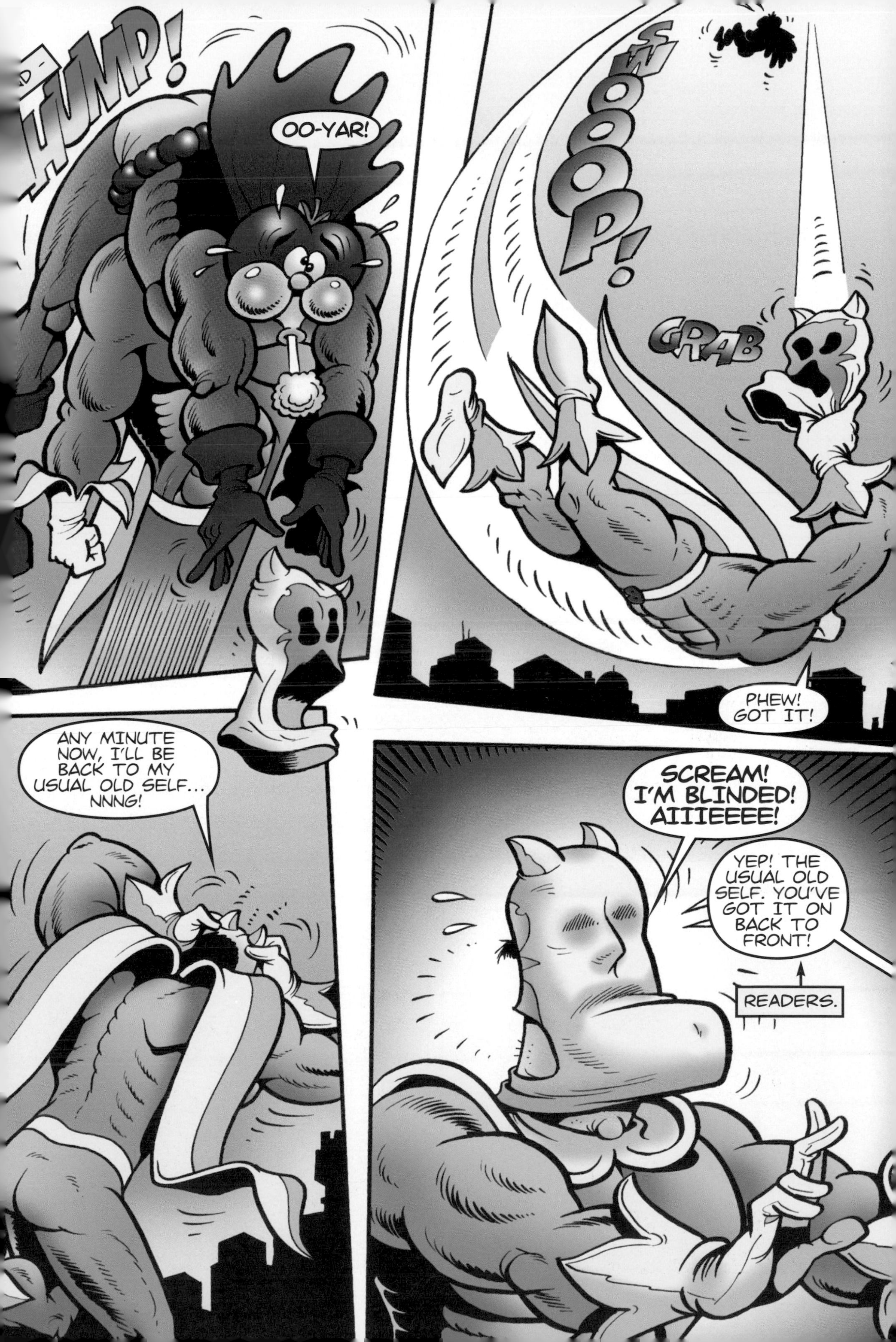
HUMP!
OO-YAR!
SWOOOOP!
GRAB
PHEW! GOT IT!
ANY MINUTE NOW, I'LL BE BACK TO MY USUAL OLD SELF... NNNG!
SCREAM! I'M BLINDED! AIIIEEEEE!
YEP! THE USUAL OLD SELF. YOU'VE GOT IT ON BACK TO FRONT!
READERS.

BLINKY'S MAD MOVIES
20th CENTURY HAMSTER
presents
ROBIN HOOD
starring Blinky as ROBIN HOOD
MY POOR, DEAR ROBIN HAS BEEN INJURED AND SOON MUST DIE. ALAS, WOE AND MORE WOE!
IF THAT DOESN'T GET ME AN OSCAR NOMINATION, NOTHING WILL, NOW GET ME A BETTER PAYING JOB, AGENT BOY!
MEANWHILE BACK IN THE FILM -
LADS, I HAVE NOT LONG TO LIVE. BURY ME WHERE MY ARROW LANDS.
AND -
TWANG!
ERM ... WANT TO TRY THAT AGAIN?
AND AGAIN? AIM FOR THE WINDOW OR WE BURY YOU ON TOP OF THE WARDROBE!
FIN

BROTHER GRIMM
HE'S A SCREAM!
HELLO, FAMILY.
I - I ALWAYS WANTED A LITTLE BROTHER FOR 'ERBERT.
SCREAMIN' 'AIRY 'AB-DABS!
LITTLE JIM'S RATTLE.
SEVERE CASE OF THE WILLIES!
TREMBLE! QUIVER! QUAKE!
DO NOT NIBBLE
HE FOLLOWED ME HOME FROM TRANSYLVANIA. I BET MR SHRIEK SENT HIM, REALLY.
GUZZLE!
KRUNCH!
BLERT!
FRIDGE
YOUR BROTHER GRIMM IS HUNGRY. TAKE HIM TO THE ZOO AND MAYBE SOMEONE WILL FEED HIM BY MISTAKE.
PRETTY PLEASE NO! YOU DON'T WANT TO GO TO THE ZOO, DO YOU, GRIMM?
BURSTING WIV MUYVERLY LUV!
SIMPER! TRILL!
DEEPLY MIFFED!
UTTERLY LIVID!
SLOOB!

HE DOES, 'ERBERT!
GOING TO THE ZOO, ZOO, ZOO! HOW ABOUT YOU, YOU, YOU?
ZOO
GIANT BLUE-TIT-EATING OCTOPUS HOUSE
DINK!
VERY RARE HUNGARIAN HAMMER-HORNED RHINOCEROS.
GALLOP! GALLUMPH!
GREAT! JUST GREAT!
WEEPSADOOZY!
MUMMY!
HURL!
WHELK HOUSE
WILLOUGHBY
VISITORS MUST NOT FEED THE JUMBOS ~ 'SPECIALLY CURRIED EGGS!
HUGE SQUELCHY DOLLOP OF SMELLY GUNGE.
SQUERT! SPLEURGE!
SKID!
?
YODDLEY-DODDLE!
VERY RARE YODELLING WOMBAT HOUSE
AHAR! A TASTY YOUNG TITBIT, JIM LAD!
I WANTED AWAY FROM GRIMM BUT THIS ISN'T WHAT I HAD IN MIND.
WARNING
ATTEMPTING TO BREAK THE "CROCODILE DOWN THE UNDERPANTS" WORLD RECORD IS VERY SILLY INDEED!
GULP!
SNACK!
FORMER STAR OF CAPTAIN HOOK.

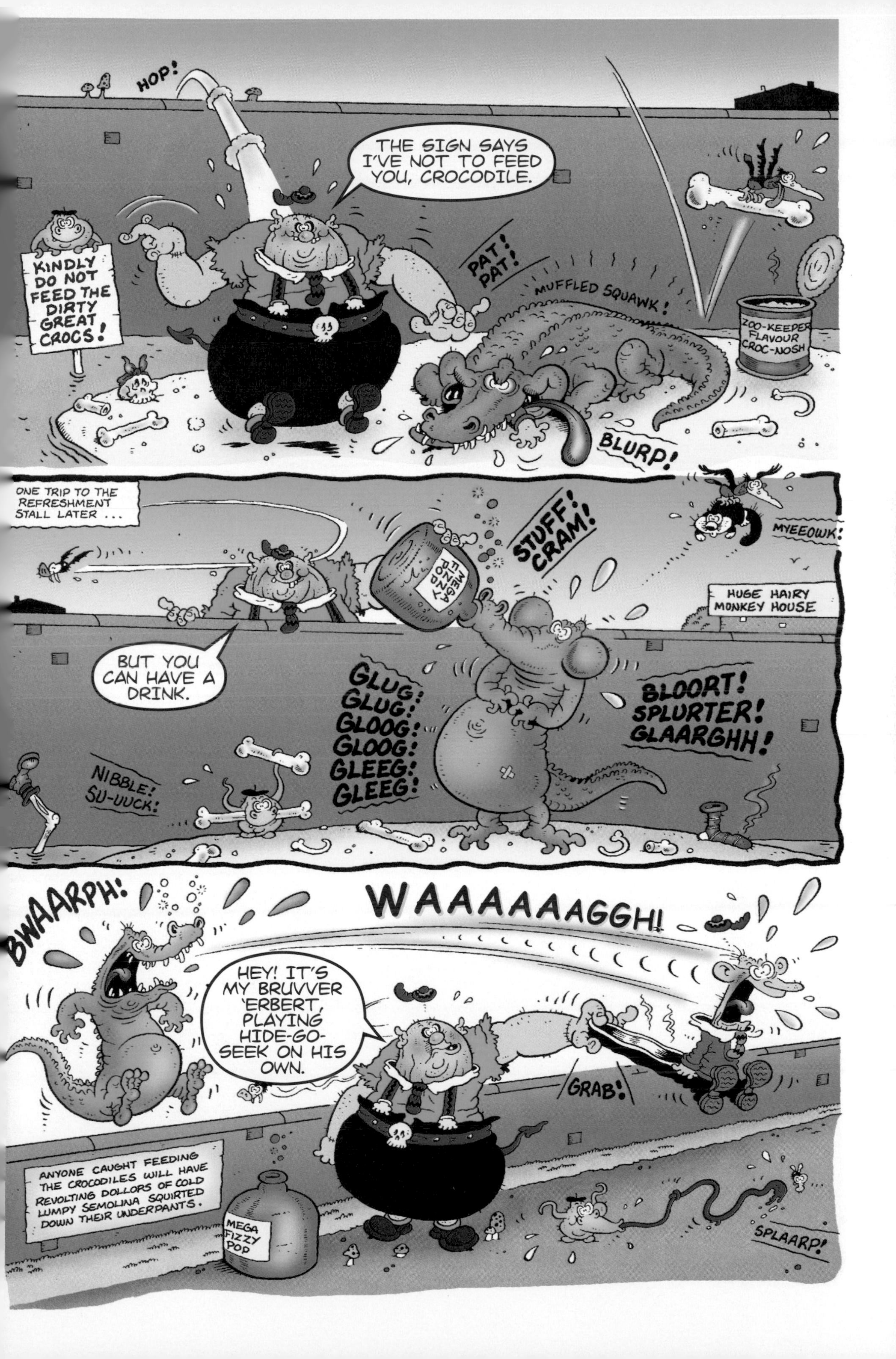
HOP!
THE SIGN SAYS I'VE NOT TO FEED YOU, CROCODILE.
KINDLY DO NOT FEED THE DIRTY GREAT CROCS!
PAT! PAT!
MUFFLED SQUAWK!
ZOO-KEEPER FLAVOUR CROC-NOSH
BLURP!
ONE TRIP TO THE REFRESHMENT STALL LATER ...
STUFF! CRAM!
MEGA FIZZY POP
MYEEOWK!
HUGE HAIRY MONKEY HOUSE
BUT YOU CAN HAVE A DRINK.
GLUG! GLUG! GLOOG! GLOOG! GLEEG! GLEEG!
BLOORT! SPLURTER! GLAARGHH!
NIBBLE! SU-UUCK!
BWAARPH!
WAAAAAAGGH!
HEY! IT'S MY BRUVVER 'ERBERT, PLAYING HIDE-GO-SEEK ON HIS OWN.
GRAB!
ANYONE CAUGHT FEEDING THE CROCODILES WILL HAVE REVOLTING DOLLOPS OF COLD LUMPY SEMOLINA SQUIRTED DOWN THEIR UNDERPANTS.
MEGA FIZZY POP
SPLAARP!

VOLCANIC FURY!
WAIT - A - MO!...
WH-WHAT'S THE MATTER, GRIMM?
BZZZZZZ
MIDGE HOUSE
MEGA FIZZY POP
CROCODILE ENCLOSURE SPONSORED BY THE HIGGINS HANDBAG CO.
BLUEBOTTLE BUTTY
CLENCH!
DRIP!
HOI! SNACKBLOKE! I WANT A WORD IN YOUR NOSTRIL.
BLAZIN' MAD!
MEGA FIZZY POP
YAIS, LARGE BUT... WELL, JUST LARGE, CHILD?
TEA
DRAG!
RUB YOUR TUM AN' LICK YOUR LIPS... THEN STUFF YOUR GOB WIV GREASY CHIPS.
THERE'S SOMETHING WORKING IN HIS PEA-BRAIN.
EARTH-SHAKING STOMP!
YOU MUST'VE SHOVED MY BROTHER IN THIS BOTTLE OF POP AND SOLD HIM TO ME.
SALAMI
MEGA FIZZY POP
WHOP! WHOP! WHOP!
SNACKS
LIMPET HOUSE
STEADY ON, GUV. YELP!
HEH! HEH! HE'S BONKERS BUT IT COULD BE KINDA FUN HAVING HIM AS A BROTHER.

DESPERATE DAN
ZZZZZ
ZZZZZ!
ZZZZZ!
SQUEAK! SQUEAK!
WHASSAT PESKY NOISE?
BETTER NOT BE ANY MICE IN THIS HOUSE. I'M COMIN' FOR YA!
SQUEAK!
SQUEAK!
WEIRD. IT'S COMING FROM DANIEL'S ROOM!

COME OUT, MOUSEY, WHEREVER YOU ARE!
ZZZ!
SQUEAK!
THWACK!
WHERE ARE YA, VERMIN? OOPS!
ZZZZ!
HE NEVER EVEN FLINCHED!
SNORE!
IT'S THOSE DANG BED SPRINGS THAT'S CAUSIN' THE RACKET. EVERY TIME HE MOVES, THEY SQUEAK!
SQUEAK!
BLART!
SCRATCH!
HE'S SCRATCHIN' A LOT TOO. WAKE UP, DANIEL! THERE MUST BE BEDBUGS ABOUT!

DON'T LET THESE BEDBUGS BITE!
SNAP!
WAKE UP, DANIEL!
SCRATCH!
SCRATCH!
SNORT!
SQUEAK! SQUEAK!
WE'LL NEVER GET THROUGH HIS TOUGH HIDE!
I SAID WAKE UP, YA BIG GALOOT!!
WHASSUP, AUNT AGGIE?
WHACK!
YOUR RICKETY BED IS KEEPING ME AWAKE. THAT'S WHAT'S UP!
THAT'S INTERESTING. ZZZZ...
DZZZZZZZZ!
GRRRR!

NEXT MORNING -
I SURE AM HUNGRY. EH?
NO BREAKFAST!
GROWL?
HUH?
GIT YORE OWN BREAKFAST. I'M AT THE SHOPS. Aggie
SUPER COMFY
TAKE IT UPSTAIRS, PLEASE, BOYS.
SURE THING, AGGIE.
WHAT'S THIS?
IT'S A TOP OF THE RANGE, DELUXE, SUPER-COMFY BED... THE FINEST ONE FROM FRED'S FURNITURE STORE. YOU NEED A NEW ONE.
CLANG!
HURMPH! I DO NOW!
THAT NIGHT -
SHUCKS! I CAN'T SLEEP!

SIGH!
MILK
I'LL GET A GOOD SLEEP, NOW!
ZZZZ!
FARP!
BURP!
DANIEL! WHAT ABOUT YOUR NEW, TOP OF THE RANGE, DELUXE, SUPER-COMFY BED... THE FINEST ONE FROM FRED'S FURNITURE STORE?
YOU HAVE IT, AUNT AGGIE. A ROUGH, TOUGH, ROOTIN'-TOOTIN' DESPERADO LIKE ME SHOULD BE SLEEPIN' UNDER THE STARS ANYWAYS!
GOODNIGHT, PARDNERS!
WINK!
SQUEAK!
KEN. H. HARRISON.

BLINKY'S MAD MOVIES
20thCENTURY AARDVARK
presents
DRACULA
starring BLINKY as THE COUNT
KRAK!
NOW I VILL NIBBLE YOUR NECK!
ERK!
I VILL GET TO SMOOCH A GIRL. TEE-HEE!
ER, IS THAT A GARLIC SARNIE?
MMM. GOT FED UP WAITING WHILE YOU WERE GIGGLING.
CHOMP!
READY NOW.
YUCK!
GARLIC WHIFF!
HONK!
HELP! I HOPE THIS IS SPECIAL EFFECTS!
I HOPE NOT, YOU PAIN IN THE NECK!
CRUMBLE!
Fin

HYDE & SHRIEK
Supper time...
I'M HAVING FLUFFY CHEESY TOAST BEFORE BEDTIME, SHRIEK.
MAGGOTY GORGONZOLA ON MOUDLY GREEN BREAD FOR ME, MASTER 'ERBERT.
DAINTY NIBBLE!
GOOEY SPLOO!
'ERBERT'S DRINKY POO
STINK! HONK! HUMMM!
Bedtime...
GOODNIGHT! SWEET DREAMS. YAWN!
BAD-NIGHT! NASTY NIGHTMARES. YAWN!
SQUEEK!
REVOLTING DIGESTIVE SQUELCH!
Soon...
BURP! BURP! GURGLE! WISH I HADN'T EATEN SO MUCH CHEESE.
SWEAT!
TOSS! TURN!

I'M SO THIRSTY. I NEED A DRINK.
SWELTER! SWEAT! STEAM!
A BIG BOTTLE OF WEIRD GREEN STUFF. WELL TASTY!
WEIRD GREEN STUFF
SWIG! CHUGGLE CHUGG!
AM I GOING TO THROW-UP?
NO! I'VE GROWN-UP!.. INTO A HORRIBLE FANG-FACED MONSTER.
ZWAAAM! VWOOPH! POOF!

SLOOBLE! SLABBER!
AND NOW I'M HUNGRY. I WANT BAKED BEANS...
GIGGLE! GURGLE! GOO!
NURK St. NURSERY SCHOOL.
GUZZLE! GOBBLE!
...HALF-BAKED HUMAN BEANS FROM THE LITTLE NUTTERS NURSERY. SLOBBER! SLOO!
TWEET! GIBBER!
WOOOOO! A GREAT SCALY THINGY IS EATING ALL MY PROBLEM INFANTS!

Meanwhile...
MOAN! GROAN! SNORE!
THRASH! FLAIL!
I FEEL SO HAPPY TODAY BUT WHY AM I WEARING THESE GLOOMY BLACK CLOTHES?
MIFFED POUT!
SIMPERING TWITTER!
THERE! THIS FRILLY PINK TUTU SUITS ME SO MUCH BETTER.

NOW I CAN SKIP AND JUMP AND DANCE AND PRANCE AMONGST THE PANSIES WITH THE PIXIES AND FAIRIES. TRAA-LAA-LAA!
WARBLE! CHIRRUP!
TWEETLE!
FROLIC! TRIP!
FLIT!
SKIP!
ROMP!
WAUGH! WHAT A NIGHTMARE!
COLD CLAMMY SWEAT!

MUMMY! I DREAMED I WAS A MONSTER AN' EATING PEOPLE ALIVE!
I DREAMED I WAS PRANCING IN A PINK TUTU WITH PIXIES AND FAIRIES!
SCREAMIN 'AIRY 'AB-DABS!
PINK TUTU AND PIXIES. COOL!
EATING PEOPLE ALIVE? ROCK ON!
LITTLE HOLEY VEST STEAMING WITH TERROR!
OINK
I'M HAVING MAGGOTY GORGONZOLA ON MOULDY GREEN BREAD.
FLUFFY CHEESE TOAST FOR ME - WITH ANY LUCK WE CAN SWOP NIGHTMARES!
GUZZLE! STUFF! CRAM!
DAINTY NIBBLE!
-TOM PATERSON-

JAK
DANDY
READY TO WIN, MORE LIKE!
READY TO PLAY, TODD?
YOU GO FIRST, THEN.
WHERE DID YOU GET THE MUD-PIES?
I GOT THE NURSERY KIDS TO HELP.
COOL!
WHAT HAPPENED? WHAT WILL YOUR PARENTS SAY?
HERE I GO!

YOU MISSED!
NOT BY MUCH!
WHATEVER! IT'S MY TURN NOW - PREPARE TO BE BEATEN!
CHAAAAARGE!!!
WHAT'S GOING ON OUT THERE?
YOU BOYS!!!

EEP.
WHAT NOW?
WE'RE IN SOOO MUCH TROUBLE!
WE'VE NO CHOICE - WE HAVE TO ATTACK!
HOW MANY MUD-PIES ARE LEFT?
UMM... 4.
THAT'LL HAVE TO DO, THEN. GIVE ME A SHOUT WHEN HE COMES OUT, OKAY?
OKAY!
WAIT FOR IT... WAIT FOR IT...

NOW!
WHAT'S THAT?
OH... NO...
AAAARRRGGGHHHH!!!
COME ON! LET'S GET OUT OF HERE!
YEAH - OR OUR NAMES WILL BE MUD!
WAYNE THOMPSON

BLINKY'S MAD MOVIES
20th CENTURY DUCK-BILLED PLATYPUS
presents
KING ARTHUR
starring
BLINKY
as
KING ARTHUR
WHOSOEVER PULLS THE SWORD FROM THE STONE WILL BIND AND UNIFY THE KINGDOM - AND WILL BE KING.
Camelot
(no riff-raff)
I SHALL DO IT, GUV!
YOU, LAD?
I SHALL UNIFY THE LAND.
GRAB!
ER... YOUR POTENTIAL KINGYNESS...
I SHALL BIND THE NATION AS ONE.
OI! ARTHUR...
STRAIN!!
I SHALL BE KING!
SIGH, WILL YOU LISTEN?

GNNN!
HEAVE!
SPROING!
GOT IT! I AM KING OF CAMELOT! FUNNY SWORD.
CRUMP!
URG!
ARGH! THAT'S 'COS IT'S PART OF THE SET, THICKY!
ER, DO I STILL GET TO BE KING?
CALL MY AGENT. I QUIT!
Fin
NICK BRENNAN

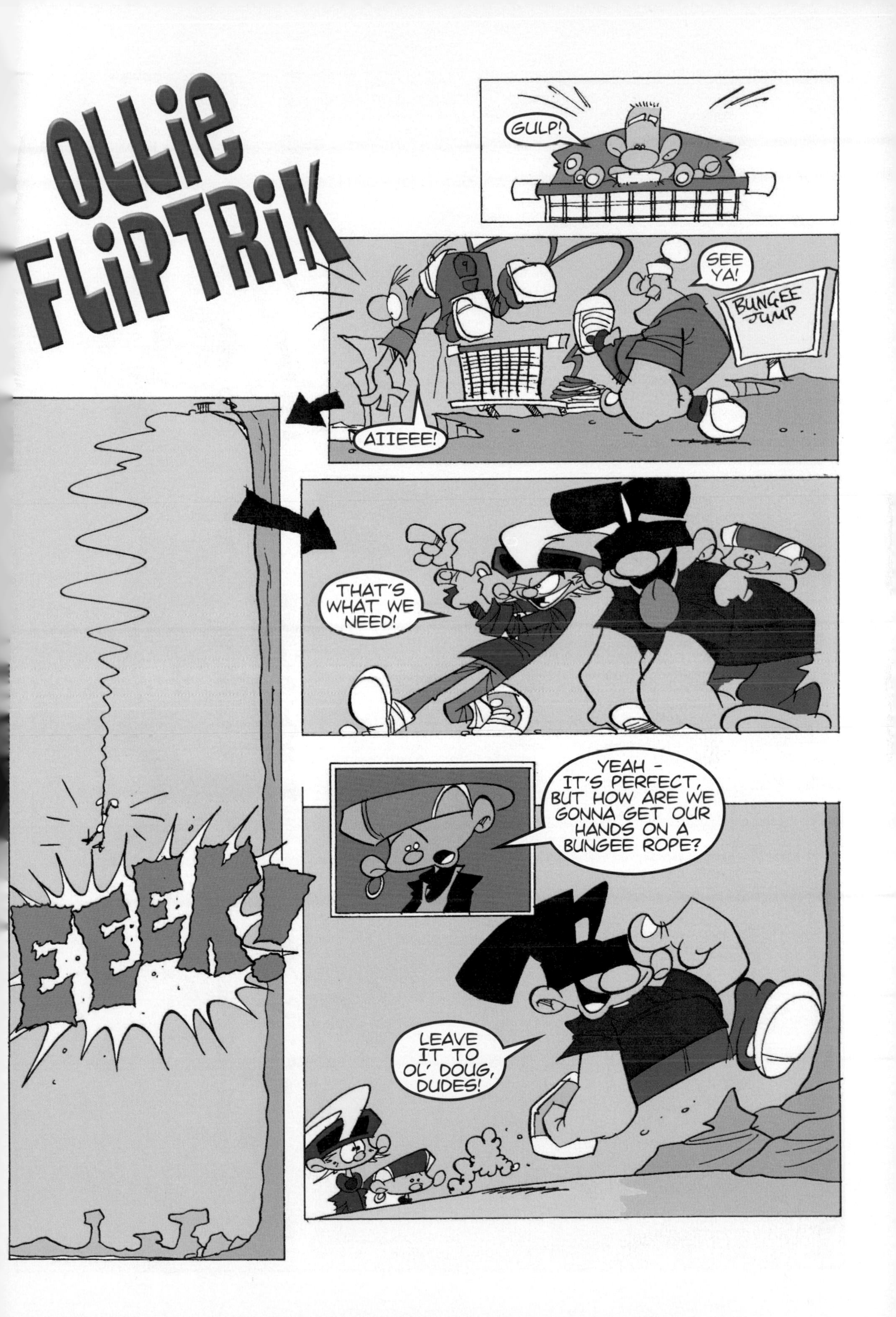
OLLIE FLIPTRIK
GULP!
SEE YA!
BUNGEE JUMP
AIIEEE!
EEEK!
THAT'S WHAT WE NEED!
YEAH - IT'S PERFECT, BUT HOW ARE WE GONNA GET OUR HANDS ON A BUNGEE ROPE?
LEAVE IT TO OL' DOUG, DUDES!

·NEWS·
SHOCK
BEANO
FAN
FOUND
etc.
MAKE WAY! COMING THROUGH! I'M A DOCTOR!
Q HERE
ACE!
LET'S GET YOU ATTACHED - THERE!
HEH-HEH!
OUT YOU GO.
SEE YA, SUCKER!
MIND THE STEP

OH, NUTS.
DID HE JUST DO WHAT I THINK HE DID?
YUP!
ONE STEP TO THE SIDE.
FTOOM!
I... I GOT IT, DUDES! TOLD YOU I WOULD!
EARTH'S CORE
APPLE CORE
YEAH, I WISH I WAS AS SMART AS YOU, DUDE!

OKAY... SOON...BE THERE!
SEEMS TIGHT ENOUGH.
SHOOKA
THWAP
WE'RE GONNA NEED SOME STRONGER TREES.
COOL! WHO'S GOING FIRST?
ARE YOU SURE THIS IS A GOOD IDEA?
LISTEN, IF YOU WANT TO PAY A FIVER TO GET INTO *OUR* SKATEPARK, YOU GO AHEAD, BUT I'M NOT!
SK8 PARK £5.00

OKAY! OKAY! BUT LET'S TEST IT FIRST.
WITH WHAT?
WELL, THIS ROCK WILL WEIGH ABOUT THE SAME AS ME. IF THE ROPE FIRES IT OVER THE WALL, WE KNOW IT'LL WORK!
NOT A BAD IDEA, DUDE!
I'D RATHER DO IT THIS WAY THAN HAVE ANYONE GET HURT, YOU KNOW.
DON'T THINK I COULD LIVE WITH MYSELF IF ANYTHING BAD HAPPENED.
BOMBS AWAY!
UH-OH!

FASTER, SMUDGER!
HEY, MY LEGS ARE ONLY LITTLE!
GULP!
AAARGH!
KRASH!
WELL, WE'RE IN!
GROO! WE DIDN'T GET OVER THE WALL...
BUT WE GOT THROUGH IT!

THE DANDY ANNUAL MAY BE OVER FOR ANOTHER YEAR...
...BUT YOU CAN KEEP YOURSELF LAUGHING WITH A LARGE HELPING OF THE DANDY COMIC EVERY WEEK.
ALL YOUR FAVOURITES WILL BE THERE WAITING FOR YOU – THE LOONIES, BAMPOTS, NUTTERS AND WACKOS WHO MAKE THE DANDY WHAT IT IS –
THE BEST!
BIGGER THAN THE BEANO!
THE DANDY
CAN YOU HANDLE IT?
STICK YOUR TONGUE OUT AT SOMEBODY TODAY! YOU KNOW YOU WANT TO!
NOT FOR WIMPS AND LOSERS
THE HORROR! THE HORROR!
FREE
SUPER-SQUELCHY SPLAT BRAIN + HARIBO HORROR MIX!
THE DANDY EVERY FRIDAY
AND DON'T FORGET YOU CAN LOG ON TO
WWW.DANDY.COM
TO KEEP IN TOUCH WITH YOUR FAVOURITE COMIC EVERY DAY...OR HOUR...OR MINUTE...

A DANDY PHOTO EXCLUSIVE!
HOME FOR CHRISTMAS!
EXCLUSIV
PICTURES
FROM BRUCE
JUNGLE
HIDEAWAY